DAVID

• PIERO BARGELLINI •

David

TRANSLATED BY ELISABETH ABBOTT

P. J. KENEDY & SONS · NEW YORK

DAVID

is a translation of *David* (Brescia, Edizioni Morcelliana, 1946).

LIBRARY OF CONGRESS CATALOG CARD NUMBER: 54–6528

PRINTED IN THE UNITED STATES OF AMERICA

CONTENTS

Foreword vii
Prologue in the Country 1
David and Goliath 9
David and Jonathan 26
David Persecuted 46
David, King of Juda 68
David, King of Israel 93
David the Sinner 120
David the Prophet 138
Bibliographical Note 164

FOREWORD

To the Florentines of the Renaissance David was the greatest of all heroes. Andrea del Castagno and Pallaiolo painted his portraits; Donatello, Verrocchio, and Michelangelo carved statues of him. David, grace combined with strength, beauty with skill, art with heroism, reality with prophecy. David, rod of Jesse, ancestor of the Madonna, forerunner of Jesus. The Florentines of the Renaissance could not have found, in one person, a better symbol of the hopes and ambitions of their city.

David slew the foolish giant, comforted the mad king, conquered enemies without number, founded the holy city, sang psalms of repentance and gratitude. He did not take up the challenge rashly, nor was he cowardly or sacrilegious when persecuted. Forsaken, he did not despair; victorious, he was not arrogant. In sin — for sin he did — he was humble; in justice, merciful; in success, sad.

Even today the figure of David seems to me as much a subject for art as in the days when the Florentines portrayed him in the attitude of swift and meditated victory.

PROLOGUE IN THE COUNTRY

EPHRATAS: "full of fruits." Encamped around the single well, in the shade of a solitary tree, the Israelites repeated the names of the Promised Land, rolling them on their tongues. Ephratas: "full of fruits."

Long, long ago the Lord Himself came down one day to walk with man in the cool of the evening. After the pleasure of wandering in the coolness came the command to march: by night preceded by a column of fire, by day by a column of smoke. For forty years, in the time between the crossing of the Red Sea and the crossing of the Jordan, the Israelites, in their feverish pilgrimage through arid lands, dreamed of a deep, cool valley where there would be food in abundance.

There no greedy sun would sear the green meadows, and

on those pastures of varied and savory grasses only the bee would flit from flower to flower before the long, trembling lip of the sheep could crop them.

From the golden bee, golden honey. From the white lamb, white milk. "Land of milk and honey." A shepherd's paradise.

When the long journey was over and they came into the promised land of their dreams, the men fell upon evil days again. The land of fragrant delights became a land of trouble and trials. Milk did not flow through the land as in the imaginings of the poet. The bee did not produce honey all year long. The earth, over which they toiled, closed, forming a hard crust and red hot, burst apart. Unable to breathe among the leaves and grass, it belched forth heat from the cracks.

Then the land ceased to be called Ephratas, but was called Bethlehem, "house of bread."

Now Booz owned the finest barley fields around Bethlehem. One morning when the harvesting was well advanced he went out to the edge of the field. Many fat shocks had already been garnered; a few bundles lay on the ground. Harsh stubble divided the mown half of the field from the other half still ripe with curving stalks. Between the coarse and shining stems the earth showed burned and creased with dark lines running in all directions.

The reapers mowed by fits and starts. It was hard to recognize in them those shepherds descended from Abraham who had tended his sheep in the Valley of Mambro, from Isaac, rich with a thousand flasks of lukewarm milk, from Jacob, moving his tents and his flocks about like clouds on earth.

Annoyed at that rustling of harsh stubble, the young

men flung the bundles down on the ground and stood over them a moment as over a defeated enemy.

"The Lord spoke to Moses, saying: Speak to all the congregation of the children of Israel, and thou shalt say to them: 'Be ye holy, because I the Lord your God am holy.'

"When thou reapest the corn of thy land, thou shalt not cut down all that is on the face of the earth to the very ground; nor shalt thou gather the ears that remain, but shalt leave them to the poor and the strangers to take. I am the Lord your God."

"Whose maid is this?" Booz asked his young men.

"She is Ruth, the Moabitess. This morning she came and hath continued even from morning until now."

She followed slowly behind the reapers, looking for any ears of corn that might fall from their hands. She wandered here and there. Where had the ear fallen? Perplexed, she stood still, then suddenly dropped on her knees. Bending down she searched about her, then straightened up again. She was the gleaner who, though she sowed not, yet did she reap; though she plowed not, yet did she harvest. On the cool edge of the field the reapers kept water in porous jugs to quench their thirst and vinegar to check their sweat, but the gleaner did not touch her lips to the water. With eyes lowered against the sun and lips ringed with white, when she was weary she turned homeward carrying her miserable bundle of ears.

And Booz and his young men marveled at Ruth's persistence in following them.

Booz went up to her. Her face was burned from the sun.

"Hear me, my daughter. Do not go to glean in any other field, and do not depart from this place. For I have charged my young men not to molest thee, and if thou art thirsty, go to the vessels, and drink. If thou art hungry, come hither and eat of the bread, and dip thy morsel in the vinegar as the others do. I know all that thou hast done to thy mother-in-law after the death of thy husband and thou art worthy to sit among our people."

Since the Law did not forbid owners to be cautious, they could advise their young men to hold tightly the swaths of corn so as not to drop any ears and even to catch the stalk with the scythe as it fell. But Booz commanded his young men to hold the sheaves loosely and to let some ears fall to the ground.

The bundle the gleaner picks is not like the bundle the mowers make. She joins ears without stems to ears with the whole stalk, grasping the mass below the knot where the stem is more delicate and fuller. The bundle becomes a star of tufts with a long tail of stalks.

After Booz had signed to his reapers, the tufts of ears grew rapidly between Ruth's trembling fingers. What a marvelous gleaning! Ruth laughed for joy. When she was thirsty, she drank. When she was hungry, she ate. And as she ate she thought with pleasure of the surprise that awaited her mother-in-law. So she set aside some of her food, admonishing herself not to be gluttonous as Booz had not been greedy.

She was thinking of her mother-in-law to whom she would carry the food that evening.

Noemi, Ruth's mother-in-law, had been one of the most beautiful and most unfortunate women in Bethlehem. Her name, Noemi, meant beautiful.

Many years before, famine had driven Noemi, her husband, and their two sons toward the land that, before it sank with Sodom and Gomorrah, had been watered and fertile. Lot, who had escaped fire and sun, still had descendants there among the Moabites. They lived at the end of the wicked lake and they had sad eyes as black as coal and beautiful women, idolized and scorned. The two sons of Noemi fell in love with two Moabite women, but, poisoned by the miasmas of the lake, they soon died, leaving their wives childless.

Then Noemi said to her two daughters-in-law: "Go ye home to your mothers; the Lord deal mercifully with you, as you have dealt with the dead, and with me."

They looked at her and their eyes were heavy with sorrow. The two dead men lay deep within them, like the two cities at the bottom of the lake.

"Do not so," said Noemi. "I am grieved the more for your distress."

The two Moabite women wept silently; and there was as much salt in their tears as in the saturated water of the lake. If the sun had not dried them out, they would have become like Lot's wife.

Noemi urged them to live. "You are still young. Return to your mothers."

In the end one of them bowed her head and turned back toward her homeland. Her name was Orpha; but the other, Ruth, would not follow her.

"Behold thy sister-in-law. Thy sister-in-law is returned to her people. She will take a husband from her own land. She will be happy. Go thou with her."

Ruth answered in a voice that showed how deeply she was hurt: "Be not against me. Whithersoever thou shalt go, I will go. The land that shall receive thee dying, in the same will I die: and there will I be buried."

When Noemi came to Bethlehem with her young daughter-in-law, all the city recognized her, and the people said: "Noemi, the beautiful, has returned."

But Noemi answered: "Call me not Noemi, but call me Mara, which is bitter, bitter as the lake that murdered my men, because I too am full of bitterness and sorrow."

In the evening Ruth returned home to Noemi with a large amount of barley and some supper. She told her she had gleaned in the field of Booz and she repeated his words: "Abide here. No one will molest you. Go not to glean in another field."

And Noemi said: "Go back tomorrow and the days to come to Booz's field and after the gleaning, when Booz winnoweth, go to his threshing floor."

The wind that blows in from the sea at sunrise reaches Bethlehem ten hours later, languid and hot; a bland and tepid little breeze that settles down over the hill stirring the air faintly without refreshing it, and the sun sets in a reddish glow. After the sun had set behind mists of blood, the sky looked very cold, far, far away, and streaked with thin clouds.

In that nocturnal breeze the corn stood out against the moonlight. But even when the moon had vanished in its turn the men did not go home. Stretching out on the mounds of chaff or on the heaps of straw, they wrapped themselves in their woolen mantles. Dawn found them there lying on the threshing floor and their beards and eyelashes were wet with dew.

One evening, following Noemi's advice, Ruth did not return home, but lingered on the threshing floor. And when the barley was winnowed and the men had stretched themselves out under the stars she came near to Booz, and, uncovering his feet, laid herself down.

Tired out from the day, Booz had fallen asleep at once,

but before dawn he awoke and was troubled to see a woman at his feet.

"Who art thou?" he asked.

"I am Ruth, thy kinswoman."

Thus discreetly, as Noemi had suggested, did she remind Booz of his obligation toward those two dead men who lay buried in the land of the Moabites, beyond the shallow and accursed lake.

Booz raised himself on his elbow and looked about him. All the men on the floor were asleep, breathing harshly under their cloaks stiff with the dew. Dawn had not yet touched the edge of the flattened earth, but up among the pallid stars the sky was turning white. Ruth's face was all soft shadows blurring her features but not obliterating them. Booz looked at that face quivering with fatigue, heard that strange yet familiar voice. Ruth lay at his feet, submissive, imploring. A sudden gleam flashed in Booz's eyes till now closed in sleep, and the blood rushed to them like light.

He arose dazed, troubled, and looked around. The woman had risen and was standing some distance away.

"Spread thy mantle, wherewith thou art covered," Booz said to her in a low tone. "And hold it with both hands."

And he emptied six measures of barley into it. Then he gathered up the corners, and, laying it upon her, led her from the threshing floor toward the house of Noemi.

In the Hebrew Laws, the command to the reapers to give no heed to fallen ears of corn is followed immediately by the precept of the levirate:

"When brethren dwell together, and one of them dieth without children, the wife of the deceased shall not marry to another; but his brother shall take her, and raise up seed for his brother:

"And the first son he shall have of her he shall call by his name, that his name be not abolished out of Israel."

The sun was striking at the gates of Bethlehem when Booz, still troubled, set out for the city. He did not enter, but halted at the gate, the seat of justice. The ancients arrived and took their places, and Booz waited until the kinsman closest to Ruth passed by. When he perceived him, he called out to him: "Ho, turn aside, sit down here."

Then requesting the attention of the ancients, he reminded them that the husband of Ruth had died without descendants. His name had not been renewed among the people of Israel. And he asked the closest kinsman whether he intended to take Ruth to wife and when the latter said he did not: "Then put off thy shoe and give it to me," Booz said.

The man took off his shoe and handed it to Booz, signifying by that act that he renounced the right of levirate.

Turning to the ancients Booz promised: "You are witnesses this day, that I have taken to wife Ruth, the wife of Mahalon, to raise up the name of the deceased in his inheritance lest his name be cut off, from among his family and his brethren and his people."

And the people of Bethlehem said: "Lo, a son is born to Noemi." No longer was she called Mara, for when she held her grandson on her lap and laid her cheek beside his glowing little face she became again Noemi, the beautiful.

And she brought up the son of Ruth and Booz and he was called Obed. He played between the furrows where Ruth had gleaned, his shouts filled the threshing floor where Ruth had watched at the man's feet. He became a man, and from him came Jesse, who was the father of David.

DAVID AND GOLIATH

SAMUEL filled a horn with oil mixed with pure myrrh, cinnamon, aromatic reed, and cassia, and with this holy mixture he set out for Bethlehem.

The ancients of that city came out to meet him, asking: "Is thy coming hither peaceable?"

It was a long time since they had looked upon the dread face of the old priest. Ever since a king ruled over Israel, a gloomy king, within a walled castle, on a throne of stone, Samuel had withdrawn to the holy city of Rama, and had never visited the scattered tribes again.

Gone were the days when the patriarchs sat outside the tent or under the lime tree or near the well, their staffs on their knees. Even Israel boasted its king. Those same Israelites, weary of humiliation and defeat, had said to

Samuel: "Give us a king who will go out before us and fight our battles for us."

Frowning and shaking his head, which had never known the touch of a razor, Samuel had disappeared. It was not mete for the Hebrews, a monotheistic people, to be monarchists. God alone ruled over all. In affirmation of this truth, the people of God had so far always denied themselves that surest instrument of earthly dominion, a king.

Now that they were again before him, Samuel reminded the ancients of the example of Gideon, who had asked God for a sign before attacking the enemy, saying: "If thou wilt save Israel by my hand, I will put this fleece of wool on the threshing floor. If there be dew on the fleece only, and if it be dry on all the ground beside, I shall know that by my hand, as thou hast said, thou wilt deliver Israel."

So Gideon — as Samuel now recalled to the ancients — spread the fleece on the threshing floor before the moon rose in the sky. He slept and, rising early in the morning, went out into the field. The floor was dry and dusty. Even the grass was still parched, as if the night had brought no coolness. It crackled underfoot and creaked sharply.

Suddenly Gideon saw that the curls of the fleece were wet and heavy with water. The wool was dark in color. And when he plunged his hands into it, it was soaked with dew.

With difficulty he raised the fleece and dragged it across the floor, leaving a clear trickle of water on the stones. Then he wrung it out in a vessel and laid it to dry all day in the sun.

And when night came, he said to the Lord: "Let not thy wrath be kindled against me if I try once more, seeking a sign in the fleece. I pray that the fleece only may be dry, and the ground wet with dew."

When, the next morning, he went out into the open, he shivered with cold. The grass was white with frost. The calice of every flower was filled to overflowing. The threshing floor looked as polished and shining as if it had been washed by rain, while the soft fleece was startlingly white against the wet stones. Plunging his hands into it, Gideon was surprised to find it as hot as the sun.

After these signs he had defeated the Amalechites and the Medians. The ancients of the tribe thereupon spoke to him in the name of all the people of Israel: "Rule thou over us, thou and thy son, and thy son's son."

With these words they offered him a kingdom and a hereditary descent. But Gideon had answered: "I will not rule over you, neither shall my son rule over you; but the Lord shall rule over you."

In spite of this reminder, the Israelites insisted upon having a king: "Behold," they said to Samuel, "thou art old, and thy sons walk not in thy ways: make us a king to judge us as all nations have."

At those words Samuel drew himself up. "Know you what shall be the right of the king that shall rule over you? He will take your sons and put them in his chariots, and will make them his horsemen and running footmen to run before his chariots. Your daughters also he will take to make him ointments, and to be his cooks, and bakers. And he will take your fields, and your vineyards, and your best olive yards, and give them to his servants. Moreover, he will take the tenth of your corn, and of the revenues of your vineyards to give his eunuchs and servants. Your servants also and handmaids, and your goodliest young men, and your asses he will take away, and put them to his work. Your flocks also he will tithe and you shall be his servants. And you shall cry out in that day from the face of the king whom you have chosen to yourselves; and the Lord will not hear you that day, because you desired unto yourselves a king."

The Israelites heard Samuel's words and were afraid; they shuddered at every threat and every danger. When he had finished, they sat silent, then hesitantly they said: "Give us a king who will go out before us and fight our battles for us. A king as all the other nations have."

Samuel reproved them, threatened them, but again they repeated even more firmly: "We desire a king who will go out before us and fight our battles for us."

The first king of Israel was Saul of the tribe of Benjamin:

Benjamin, rapacious wolf, in the morning will devour his prey
And in the evening he will divide the spoils.

Handsome of face, tall of stature, Saul stood head and shoulders above all the men of his tribe. His rule began under happy auspices. "Whithersoever he turned himself," says the Bible, "he overcame." At last the Hebrews had a king who could fight a battle and win it.

He created royalty and became jealous of his own creation. Everything that might threaten or weaken his royal power aroused his suspicion. Spear in hand, seated on a throne of stone with his back to the wall in fear of treachery, Saul kept watch over any attempt against his power and his dignity. It seemed to him that an earthly monarchy could not be established under the tutelage of priesthood and in absolute respect of the law.

Because Saul interpreted in his own way the commands

of God Samuel cursed him: "The Lord hath rejected thee from being king over Israel."

Frightened by this curse, Saul said to Samuel: "Come, come with me. Let us worship the Lord."

But Samuel refused to pardon him or to help him: "I will not return with thee, because thou hast rejected the words of the Lord."

And he was about to leave but, with an imperious gesture, Saul laid hold of his cloak. With his great strength Saul sought to hold back the old man and the cloak was torn. Turning around, Samuel said: "As thou hast torn in twain the cloak" — and his slow words and gestures emphasized his condemnation plainly and fearfully — "As thou hast torn in twain the cloak, so the Lord hath rent the Kingdom of Israel from thee this day and hath given it to one who is better than thee."

There were no witnesses to this scene. Priest and king were alone and face to face. At the moment Saul did not grasp the gravity of the divine condemnation. One thought filled his mind to the exclusion of all others: his desire to reign. He still believed that his power derived from men and that the stability of the kingdom rested on human respect and outward dignity. "I have sinned," he said, "yet honor me now before the ancients of my people, and before Israel."

And Samuel honored him before the people, but after that he turned his thoughts to Him who was the true king of the true kingdom.

Among the ancients of Bethlehem who came forth to greet Samuel on his sudden return was Jesse, the grandson of Booz. With the help of his eight sons and three daughters, he cultivated his fields of barley and corn.

Samuel turned to him. He wished to see the eight sons, because it had been revealed to him that one of their number would be king; that he must call them to him and anoint the one that God would show to him.

And when he saw the eldest son of Jesse, Samuel looked thoughtful and uncertain. Eliab, a beautiful youth, with his great height and proud carriage, could have rivaled Saul himself. But the Lord said to Samuel: "Look not on his countenance, nor on the height of his stature. Man seeth those things that appear, but the Lord beholdeth the heart."

Then seven sons of Jesse passed before the seer, one after the other. "Are here all thy sons?" asked Samuel.

"There remaineth yet a young one, David, who is out in the pasture."

"Send for him and fetch him, for we will not sit down till he come hither."

The eighth son of Jesse tended his father's sheep, not because he was incapable of better things. His brothers perhaps could endure harder work, but they were no nimbler and no stronger than he. He could sing and play the harp. Nor had he his equal in running, in drawing the bow, or in striking with the shepherd's crook.

While not handsome, he had copper-red hair, an olive skin, and gray-green eyes. Deep lines between his lips and his aquiline nose lent his face an expression of melancholy until it broke into a broad radiant smile.

As he played the harp and sang he did not even listen to himself. Absent-minded, with his thoughts far away, he wandered about with distracted eye. When Samuel asked for him, he was staring out across the grassy border at the fields yellow with ripe corn. There, in the burning heat of the sun and in the dust of summer, his older brothers gleaned the sheaves where Ruth had once gathered ears of corn.

Suddenly he heard one of those voices which, in the country, sound like mournful wails. Mysteriously they are born and die in silent distances, but as they pass they bring dismay to the lonely soul.

David leapt up from the meadow where a solitary tree spread its shade like a cloak and, shaking off the lassitude of the pasture, he arrived breathless at his father's house.

Samuel received him and poured oil on his dusty hair. The young shepherd felt the delicacy of that perfumed unction cleansing the sweat on his forehead, while the myrrh brought relief and coolness to his neck.

His head with its close-cropped hair, curly at the top, rose lightly from his shoulders. His clear eyes turned to his brothers and his father in pleased surprise. That anointing was a mark of predilection, signifying that the harpist had been chosen, over his farmer brothers, for religious consecration. He was feeling slightly giddy from the aromatic oil when he thought he heard a soft voice saying: "Thou shalt be King."

Frowning, he looked up at Samuel, and a sudden excitement gripped him. Samuel was gazing impassively into the distance. His lips were firmly closed and his hands were clasped tightly at his knees.

Saul, meanwhile, sat on his throne growing gloomier and sadder than ever. Outwardly he defended his threatened royalty rigidly, almost to the point of cruelty. But behind that firmness and that painful fixity no one knew the devastation that ravaged the soul of the handsomest man in Israel.

Bewildered and alert, with his forehead pale and damp,

he sat upon the throne of stone, and his eyes stared but his mind did not see. His glassy pupils were turned inward on those depths of his soul where images rushed past silently like certain stones that disappear in the clefts of stony mountains.

And God turned his face from him. He turned his face from him as the light turns from the world and the sadness of shadows touch the mountains for a little while with violet lip before darkness fills the lowlands with its terrors.

Saul lived in a vacuum. Every pleasure he had was tarnished with distrust. It was all useless and at the same time all painful. Important matters seemed paltry to him, and unimportant ones took on fantastic proportions in his lonely mind.

The king's royal palace was a military barracks. The men of Benjamin, clever slingers and famous archers, were neither artists nor orators. In the presence of the melancholy king they were silent. And in that silence the king's melancholy turned to madness.

At last the servants said to him: "An evil spirit surrounds thee. If thou wilt, let us go in search of a man who knows how to play the harp, so that thou mayest have relief."

They searched throughout all the tribe of Benjamin for a harpist. Every Benjamite had made a sling either out of leather or horse-hair. But no one had ever made himself a harp with bones and the gut of a ram. Therefore they were obliged to turn to Juda and in all that tribe there was no finer harpist than the youngest son of Jesse.

David came to the court of Saul on an ass loaded with bread, a skin of wine, and a kid. Whoever appeared at the palace, even when summoned thither, must win the king's favor with gifts of that sort. But David won the king more by his presence than by his gifts.

Young David was strong and lithe. His hair made a halo of red flame around his sunburned face, and below his forehead his clear eyes tamed the laughter that flashed from his shining white teeth.

Seldom did one find golden or tawny hair, blue or greenish eyes among the Hebrews and the population of Canaan. Eyes like David's in particular, light eyes, bewitching and compelling, were feared as evil omens. Those eyes held a seductive power, and to ward off their fascination people carried amulets of the same color.

Though David had a delicate skin, his body was strong. Agile and light, he carried himself with a natural elegance. As he sang, he accompanied himself on the *kinnor* mounted on a bone tuning fork, with ten jingling strings.

At the sound of that young voice Saul's mind cleared and he remembered his own youth. But what he saw before him was the kindly face of Cis, his father, worried about the fate of his asses, and not the face of this beautiful young boy. And he saw again Samuel's fatherly glance as he carefully spread the bed on the terrace for the first King of Israel.

As a sign of his favor Saul therefore sent the unloaded ass back to Jesse with this message: "David shall remain in my service for he has already found favor in my eyes."

In those years when David dwelt at the court of the king as harpist he had his encounter with Goliath.

Goliath belonged to the dread army of Philistines, a people Aegean in origin, who lived along the coast and on the islands — which is why the Philistines called themselves "men of the North and of the sea." Tall men with smooth hair, they were good sailors, good farmers and, above all, excellent soldiers. The Hebrews feared them because they were armed with chariots and because in a hand-to-hand fight they overpowered them by their height. The scouts sent out by Moses were therefore not lying when they said that the Promised Land was populated by giants.

Before he crossed the Jordan, Moses had selected twelve scouts, one from each tribe, and had sent them to reconnoiter the country. Summer was then fading into autumn. The figs looked like bags of honey. The grape was turning black. In one of the lush valleys two scouts had gathered a bunch of grapes so large that they had to hoist it on a bar and carry it back to the camp on their shoulders.

When the Israelites saw those grapes they shouted for joy, but the scouts told them: "The men who live in that land are tremendously strong; their cities vast and walled. We saw there the descendants of Enac, men of extraordinary stature."

The Hebrews continued to picture to themselves those giants raising enormous bunches of grapes to their dreadful mouths and they were afraid. But Caleb, the scout from the tribe of Juda, turning against his companions, promised that he would devour those people like bread. Later on, when put to the test, even the teeth of the young lion gnawed in vain on the white Philistine bone. The tribe of Caleb was forced to withdaw toward the mountain, leaving the plain and the seashore to the Philistines.

Few in number, but well organized in their fortified pentapolis, and ruled by warrior princes, the Philistines maintained their dominion over the most fertile part of the land of Canaan which they called Philistina or Palestine. Against their army, the army of Israelites, poorly equipped, badly organized, and badly led, menacing only because of their numbers, but as incoherent as a herd of cattle, struck and fought in vain. Issuing victorious from all the wars, the Philistines imposed new tributes and burdens on the Israelites.

Compared with those tall, white-skinned warriors, the short, dark, curly-haired Hebrews offered a strange contrast. "In comparison with them," they said, "we are crickets." But if the Philistines were taller than the Israelites, there was one of their own company who surpassed all his comrades in height and strength. His name was Goliath. A strong, large-limbed man; a very castle of bone encased in powerful muscles, he had a big, stupid face, with few hairs on his chin, and a low forehead above small, piglike eyes.

He made light of his strength and was in the habit of tossing heavy weapons about like toys. He was always trying to pick a quarrel with his comrades for the fun of it and with his enemies with the idea of adding to his renown.

The two hostile armies were drawn up facing each other, but had not broken camp. From their positions on either side of a valley covered by a growth of terebinth and its thick and magical shade, they watched each other suspiciously.

Taking advantage of the truce, Goliath had challenged an Israelite champion to a duel. He dreamed, with his childish smile, of making himself famous in that valley named for the terebinth.

At crack of dawn, therefore, with that hope in mind and still wearing that fatuous smile, he dressed himself in his armor as carefully as if he were going into battle. His comrades stared at him incredulously. They knew the temperament of the Israelites. Goliath would never find a competitor among the legions of Saul. A stone or two shot from a hidden catapult might fall near him, but no enemy champion would come out against him.

Goliath paid no attention to his comrades' ironical glances. As he buckled on his cuirass and fastened his greaves, he raised his eyebrows, and his low forehead filled with short irregular lines.

Shading his eyes, he peered sharply ahead, and passing out beyond the palisade, he went down into the grassy valley. His shadow moved before him, reversed on the meadow. That big swaying figure of his delighted him. His widespread legs formed a powerful triangle, and when he stood still, the shadow of the spear descended sharply between his two firmly planted feet.

"Choose out a man of you and let him come down and fight hand to hand," he roared. "If he be able to fight with me and kill me, we will be servants to you; but if I prevail against him, and kill him, you shall be servants and serve us."

Silence. No one answered. The stream which divided the valley, and beside which Goliath had stopped, gurgled over the stones. Three times Goliath repeated his challenge. Then he stood and waited. The terebinth rustled lightly; the water sang. In the silence, Goliath felt rage boiling within his breast. "Cowards," he roared. "Today I have dishonored Israel."

Up the hill he climbed again, though this time with more difficulty than when he went down it, and returned to camp in a fine fury. But that evening after he had rested he put on his armor again, careless of his comrades' mocking laughter. Again he went down into the valley and repeated his challenge. Then, as he turned back, he repeated the same words: "Today I have dishonored Israel."

And this he did, methodically, for forty days. Eighty times he buckled on his armor, eighty times he went down into the valley of the Terebinth, eighty times he repeated the challenge, and eighty times declared that he had dishonored Israel.

For forty days he went through the same motions. And the only difference was that in the morning he arrived at the stream preceded by his own shadow and in the evening he was faithfully followed by it. At midday and during the afternoon he rested and waited for the breeze to spring up so that he might arise, put on his armor and go off to repeat the challenge that was never accepted. . . .

Goliath inspired terror not only by his gigantic build; his armament was also formidable. His head was protected by a helmet of hammered brass, rounded the better to avoid blows. A cuirass of scales, weighing five thousand sicles, which is equal to one hundred and sixty-five pounds, protected his chest and hips. His legs were encased in greaves, and a leather shield covered with brass defended him from shoulders to knees. The pole of his spear looked like a weaver's beam, the iron tip alone weighing six hundred sicles, or twenty-two pounds. Each piece of armor was a masterpiece in itself, for the Philistines had introduced the metal industry into the region that dripped of milk and honey.

The Bible says that the descendants of Cain built the first walled city, and made the first hammered work. The Philistines belonged to the race of metalworkers descended from Tubalcain. They were also smiths and made instruments for peace and for war out of iron. They forged spades and spears, ground scythes and swords, made plows and scythed war chariots. The chariots in particular, which they used in battles on the plains, terrified the Hebrews, who were unable to put either cavalry or heavily armed warriors into the field.

By sheer force and skill the Philistines had gained control of all the iron wrought in Palestine. "In all the land of Israel," says the Bible, "there was no smith to be found, for the Philistines had taken this precaution, lest the Hebrews should make them swords or spears." And again, and even worse: "All Israel went down to the Philistines, to sharpen every man his ploughshare, and his spade, and his axe, and his rake."

If a shepherd wanted to shear his sheep, no matter how far away he was, he was obliged to go down the mountains of Engaddi and knock at the gates of the Philistines to procure scissors and shearing knives. If he wanted to mow, the Hebrew whose barley field adjoined the cave where his ancestors were buried must first carry his plows to the anvils of the Philistines. The Philistines in the land of Canaan, with their walled cities closed by iron gates (those gates which Samson tore from their hinges and loaded on his shoulders), with their shops of Cretan ceramics, were the exponents of a material and industrial civilization. In contrast, the Israelites represented a religious idea, a spiritual civilization.

"What shall be given to the man that shall kill this Philistine, and shall take away the reproach from Israel?" David asked the men that stood around him.

"The king will enrich with great riches the man that shall slay him, and will give him his daughter, and will make his father's house free from tribute in Israel," was the answer.

David had never fought against any man. In the pastures

he carried only a staff and a sling. At court the only thing he touched was the harp. No weapon had ever spoiled his comeliness, no battle armor adorned it. He was a charmer. The fresh, clear light of his eyes bewitched, his words persuaded, and his song moved all who heard it. Already the royal family had fallen under the fascination of his spell.

He himself was aware of that mysterious power he exercised over the heart of the king and the minds of his household. Sometimes at night it troubled and saddened him. Therefore early in the morning he was wont to go out from the royal palace, and sing by himself, unself-consciously, as when he was a shepherd. The rising sun and the moon, misty as it waned, restored his serenity and simplicity.

One morning he saw Goliath coming down into the valley of the Terebinth. As the giant strode over the muddy field, the light cast greenish reflections on the red of his brass armor. At that sight David longed to be a brave warrior. He wanted to go out against the giant, armed only with his strength and fearlessness, and match himself against him.

What, he thought scornfully, was the seduction of music and the charm of comeliness compared to prowess at arms? He longed to wash away the dreams of the night, and once more, spotless and clean, to face Goliath and risk his life in a test of manly courage.

Saul tried to dissuade him from the dangerous undertaking.

"Thou art but a shepherd," he told him, "but he is a warrior from his youth."

And still, David remembered other fights he had had, and in that moment he recalled them with pleasure. "Thy servant kept his father's sheep and there came a lion or a bear and took a ram out of the midst of the flock, and I pursued after them, and struck them, and delivered it out of their mouth."

He smiled as he thought of that bear he had struck, and his eyes held a faraway expression so that he saw no one around him. From that moment he faced the danger coolly, neither shrinking from it nor attracted by it. He was the very picture of pride, but Saul was troubled by his nakedness.

Saul, too, was well armed. The Philistines had ordered all the Hebrews to disarm and when the day of battle came — it is written in the Book of Kings — "there was neither sword nor spear found in the hand of any of the people except Saul and Jonathan his son."

In some ways Saul, of the tribe of Benjamin, was a counterpart of the Philistines. He was tall and strong, and he, too, relied on the power of arms. He pitted strength against strength, weapons against weapons, iron against iron, brass against brass.

Troubled by David's nakedness, he wanted to clothe him in armor. On the young man's head he set the helmet of brass; he fastened on him the cuirass, he buckled on the sword. He made of David a miniature Goliath.

David tried to walk in that harness, but he was not accustomed to it, and he said to Saul: "I cannot go thus for I am not used to it."

Laying aside his armor, he took up his staff and went down into the valley of Terebinth. The sun beat on his face, the dew bathed his feet. Lightly and serenely he passed through that familiar countryside. When he came to the ford of the rushing river, he chose five flat and well-polished stones and put them in his shepherd's scrip. Just so, Joshua, when he crossed the Jordan, had ordered his men to select twelve square and heavy stones to build the first altar in the promised land. David, instead, chose five round stones as flat as cakes. Those stones cut swiftly through the air, swerving neither to the right nor to the left.

When Goliath saw David before him, with his legs bare and shoulders uncovered, he laughed at him. An expression of irony appeared on the giant's childish face and his eyes disappeared between his eyelashes and his cheeks. Rough, ignorant bullies, glorying in their strength, are often facetious and laugh at their own jokes. So Goliath said to David: "Am I a dog that thou comest to me with a staff?"

That was the most his sarcasm could muster. But at once he passed from irony to invective or rather to curses in the name of his gods.

David gave no sign that he had heard, but his boyish face took on a firm and manly expression. And when he spoke his words were neither ironical nor angry, but a sort of credo uttered with faith:

"Thou comest to me with a sword, and with a spear, and with a shield: but I come to thee in the name of the Lord of hosts, the God of the armies of Israel, whom thou hast defied. This day, and the Lord will deliver thee into my hand, and I will slay thee, and take away thy head from thee: and I will give the carcasses of the army of the Philistines this day to the birds of the air, and to the beasts of the earth: that all the earth may know that there is a God in Israel.

"And all this assembly shall know, that the Lord saveth not with sword and spear: for it is his battle, and he will deliver you into our hands."

He took up the sling. The stone cut the air with a hiss, and the giant, struck on the temple, fell face downward, full length between the tree and the brook.

DAVID AND JONATHAN

Saul slew his thousands
And David his ten thousands.

As THEY sang and danced, the women of the cities of Israel repeated this refrain, and Saul was hurt by it. He listened intently. From afar off tenuous feminine voices, the clear voices of women, came to him:

Saul slew his thousands
And David his ten thousands

In their rejoicing the women, more perfidious and innocent than young girls, added fresh anguish to the king's madness. Saul would not have been so suspicious at the sound of revolt as at those voices. Against enemies and rebels he would have fought with all the strength of his great height and with the majesty of his power; but those voices that filtered between the songs of warriors, those voices as tender as young blades of grass, transparent as jets of water, insinuating and fleeting, made him tremble with jealousy.

The women admired David. David was grace that had conquered force. They loved David because he was descended from a family of famous women. In the Davidian genealogy, Tamar, Rahab, and Ruth were the personification of wisdom, prudence, and loyalty. No man of the family had attained the fame of those three foreign women.

The women also admired David because women are the ones who teach and appreciate heroism. Men make warriors: from men one learns dexterity, intrepidity, and fidelity, but from woman, courage and daring. Courage is like a sudden illumination and is born from prudence. Courage often looks like imprudence, but it is merely sublime prudence. Dedications, vows, and renunciations are the proud moments of courage in which woman dominates and subjugates man. Moments not at variance with prudence, they, but the secret and unforeseen reactions of that virtue.

There is no one like a woman to inspire deeds of unexpected courage by that continual warmth of good works which is the very substance of prudence. And there is no one in the world like a woman from whom one can learn the heroism in virtue. In virginity and in maternity, in love and in affection, she transforms danger and terror into grace. She transfigures sorrow into beauty; brutality into kindness.

Only where women are present do heroes arise. No

generous deed is born alone, and man's courage is stimulated by woman's admiration for the exploits her imagination weaves with amazing rapidity.

In Israel women reared their sons carefully. Under the patriarchal system the sons of the same mother felt bound in the closest relationship. In their turn the brothers of the same mother defended and watched over their sisters jealously. The common father guided and judged. Individual mothers suffered and consoled. They chose their sons' names, and their grown sons recognized their authority and honored them.

For this reason cities were called "mothers in Israel," and "maternal breast" signified the tribe from which a man issued. The highest praise a man could receive was "Blessed be the woman who is thy mother."

Saul came from a tribe of men skilled in arms, and the women of Benjamin lacked the charm of those strangers, Canaanites and Moabites, who had come into the family of Juda. There is no sign of any women around the figure of Saul.

Music inspired Saul with silent awe, but he could not play any instrument. To David even the technique of the art was a delight in which he reveled. Saul destroyed; David created anew. In Saul the man, stripped of his royal appurtenances, we see the tragic nostalgia of a human being who, though he can be happy only in forgetfulness, yet is unable to lose himself even in pleasure.

The princess, whose dowry David had paid with Goliath's bloody head, was called Merob. Nothing is known of her but her name. She was Saul's eldest daughter and no doubt she resembled her father, from whom perhaps she inherited her stern and melancholy features. Seen in the light of the role history assigns her, she appears to have been an austere and haughty girl who apparently was not drawn to David, the young conqueror, in his triumph. That stranger at court must have left her completely indifferent, if not even with a feeling of aversion. David held sway over her sick father, and Merob may have felt that there was something insidious and untrustworthy in that enchanting music.

She was Saul's eldest daughter: that daughter who, at the first signs of maturity, supplanted the mother in the father's affection and tenderness. Perhaps she was one of those girls who dislike being a woman and are happy only by the side of the father who needs them.

Her eyes held the same expression as Saul's. She was a prize to the valiant; and indifferent to their fate, at the side of her lonely father (she, too, was lonely) Merob was every inch the daughter of the king.

In her David saw not love, but glory. For her he had risked death, but perhaps not even he knew what light could shine from her indifferent eyes, nor how her tightly closed lips could smile. Of her he knew only what we know: her name and her relationship to the king.

"And it came to pass at the time when Merob the daughter of Saul should have been given to David, that she was given to Hadriel the Molathite to wife."

Saul therefore refused to give David his eldest daughter, Merob. He would not have the shepherd, the harpist, for his son-in-law.

A very ancient Oriental tradition traces the line of succession to the throne through the female descent. The stranger who succeeded in marrying the daughter of the king would inherit the throne. Women (not men) still tell stories of those young heroes who asked for a loaf and found a kingdom.

The idea of an unknown hero who comes to a strange

country and wins royal privileges is not so ingenuous as it appears in the legends. The king always comes from a race of heroes and leaders. When he stirs the imagination of that people over which he will later rule, he is only the hero. His background and the land of his birth may be unknown. His true birth, in the new land and in the realm that will be his, is the deed that makes him famous. With that deed his history begins. The preceding days of his mysterious life belong to the man. Those that follow belong to the king.

Succession to the throne on the distaff side assures the dynasty of an uncommon type of man, men, moreover, readily acceptable to the king and to the people. For an outsider to distinguish himself in a hostile land, for him to attain the throne with the help of the precious and delicate hand of the king's daughter, he must show himself valiant in every test and winning in all his actions.

David had come to Gabaa as a stranger, from the tribe of Juda. At court he had become known through his art, among the people by his fearlessness. His music had won the heart of the king; his victory over Goliath the admiration of the people.

Of his life before this time we know little. Saul could remember his peasant origin. David never recalled his life as a shepherd. David was known at once as the slayer of Goliath.

> Saul slew his thousands
> And David his ten thousands.

The first line put an end to Saul's exploits. With the second, David's fame began to spread throughout Israel. But the shepherd's beginning was so much more glorious than the old king's end. Saul had cause to be worried and jealous. He feared lest the harpist outstrip him in the people's favor, even perhaps rob him and his descendants of the kingdom.

To the first King of Israel dynastic problems, new to the mind of every Israelite, assumed gigantic proportions. He had been chosen king. Who would succeed him on that throne of stone backed against the wall? When Samuel consecrated Saul, he had not spoken of any monarchical succession. And later in his curse he had threatened: "The Lord hath rent the Kingdom of Israel from thee this day and hath given it to one near thee who is better than thee." But who was this man near the king?

Perhaps the anointing of David had not been well enough concealed. Perhaps David himself had told someone his suspicion of the meaning of the remark that sprang almost involuntarily from the lips of Samuel.

Saul would have liked to leave his kingdom to his son. But the history of Israel inclined toward the rule of the spirit. Today we would know no more of that history than we do of those disreputable hordes of Bedouins who roamed between deserts and pasture lands; and between the dynasties of the Pharaohs and the Babylonian emperors it would have left no more impression than a scarab between two lumps of basalt, if, through Abraham's religious guidance, the Hebrew nation had not obeyed the voice of divine inspiration. Saul's plans to continue his dynasty which his confused mind mulled over again and again had neither weight nor significance. David's inspired singing put an end to them once and for all.

The son Saul would have liked to see follow him on the throne was Jonathan, the only man who stood by his father's side well armed, among all those Israelites without spears and swords. Jonathan was a warrior, too, and he possessed the finest attributes of the warrior: courage and generosity.

In comparison with the Philistines, the Hebrews showed little spirit of aggression unless aroused and incited by some heroic deed. Even before David slew Goliath and by intimidating the Philistines encouraged the Israelites, Jonathan, too, had won fame by beginning a day of battle with a bold gesture.

The armies were drawn up opposite one another, neither side having made any move to open battle. The Philistines held the best positions, fortresses of rocks piled one on top of the other on which they had stationed garrisons of men-at-arms.

But one quiet morning, when only the sentinels were keeping an eye on the tree tops of spears, Jonathan said to his shield bearer: "Come, let us go over to the garrison of the Philistines which is on the other side."

Unnoticed, he crossed the open space between the two camps, and came to the foot of a rock difficult to scale. Jonathan, who was as religious as his father, entrusted to God the outcome of that emprise: "If they call us we shall go up because the Lord hath delivered them into our hands. This shall be a sign to us."

Secure in their superiority, the Philistines invited him to scale the position, and Jonathan leapt up on the rock. From a distance the Israelite sentinels gave warning of the brief struggle. The little cluster of armed men clinging to that rock looked as if it were tossed about by the wind. The sentinels could see soldiers falling and that whirlwind sweep into camp carrying disorder and confusion in its train.

Saul asked the name of the bold warrior who had put the Philistine army to rout singlehanded, but no one could answer him, for Jonathan had stolen out secretly and had told no one of his plan. Thereupon the king summoned all his warriors in review. And not till they were assembled did he notice that Jonathan, his first born, was missing. He ordered his men to follow the enemy and all day long the Israelites pursued the Philistines in the woods as one hunts rabbits.

That very day Jonathan unwittingly violated Saul's oath. Before giving the order to pursue the enemy, Saul had promised God that no fighter would touch food all day long. Full of courage, Jonathan was far away and knew nothing of the vow. As he passed a thicket, he saw a comb of wild honey. Plunging a stick into it, "his face lighted up," and he refreshed himself. He had been fighting since morning, and when the others were still stretched out under their tents, he was already scaling the clefts of the rock crowned with enemy warriors.

When Saul heard this, he was about to punish him, but the whole army rose up against him: "As the Lord liveth," said the sons of Israel, "there shall not one hair of his head fall to the ground, for he hath wrought with God this day."

Everyone loved Jonathan. He was the finest swordsman in the kingdom. To Jonathan's valor Saul owed many of his victories and to his modesty many of his triumphs. He was the first to lead the attack in battle, the last to withdraw. For himself he never reserved any privilege, save that of fighting at the head of the army.

But in peace, in his father's royal palace, in that atmosphere of tragic fatality which hung over the royal family, he kept himself in the background. He would take no part in government matters. Perhaps he felt incapable. He was enthralled by David's music, enchanted by his words. He realized that he could not do the things David performed with such careless ease. And, as with all melancholy natures, his thoughts leapt from one impossible exploit to another impractical plan.

As the companion of his daydreams he chose David, spending the exhausting noon hours with him talking feverishly, intoxicated by his own words, until he wearied himself into drowsiness. Long discourses followed by extraordinarily long silences, weariness by enervation, lyric flights by complete prostration. Toward evening their heads were heavy and their spirits tired. David scarcely touched the harp, and Jonathan drooped in deepest melancholy, like one who is vanquished.

Saul was more fearful for Jonathan and for his succession to the throne than for himself. "As long as the son of Jesse lives, I shall not be secure, nor shall you, nor your kingdom," Saul said, and looked at Jonathan, hoping to read scorn and anger on his son's face. Instead, something happened that flung the old king into a rage — something that deranged his mind even more. Taking off his own cloak, Jonathan placed it around David. He unbuckled his sword from his side and gave it to David. He slipped the bow off his shoulder and held it out to David. He presented David with his own belt.

Jonathan was not suspicious of David, neither could he bring himself to fear him or to despise him. He loved him, and according to the ritual of friendship, he deprived himself to clothe his friend. Friendship is not a possessive, lustful love seeking its own good, but a harmonious love seeking the good of another. Not love of union, but love of communion. And to the extent that friendship is superior to love just so Jonathan seemed to be above envy and suspicion.

In Saul, blood spoke. In Jonathan, friendship. "David is a threat to your throne," Saul said.

"Why shall he die?" Jonathan replied. "What hath he done?"

At those words Saul raged, but his son did not rebel. With the docility of the victim he followed him, but was not with him. He would have followed him to death, falling by his side, but always separated.

Just as the Lord had withdrawn from Saul's mind, so the son, who was a true gift of God, drew away from him. Saul saw him stretch out at David's side, and his grief was mixed with the mists of madness.

Close to Jonathan, but far removed from her father, came Michol, the king's second daughter, the sister of Merob. Michol must have been very different from her elder sister. She was warmhearted and keen of mind like her brother. Imaginative and passionate, with no thought of her father's anguish and suspicion, she had perhaps approved in her heart the refrain the women of Israel sang.

And she, too, had loved the hero who brought back Goliath's armor on his slender shoulders, but her love had been more secret and of a different sort than Jonathan's. To her David's red hair, among the black curls of the Israelites, was like a flame. The songs, to the accompaniment of the harp that brought peace to Saul, robbed Michol of hers as she listened breathlessly to them in her rooms.

Her passion burned in secret, for the slayer of Goliath belonged to her elder sister. And she gazed with feverish eyes at Merob's cold eyes and that impassive face on which no trace of pain or bewilderment ever appeared.

Michol, on the other hand, was a dreamer like her

brother. She dreamed of the impossible: that David might see her and might sing for her. She did not envy her sister for, like Jonathan, she was incapable of wishing anyone harm. She suffered, however, and had always suffered because of that disdainful and privileged sister. She had grown up almost in awe of Merob's superiority. The elder sister was haughty and domineering, and Michol, impulsively submissive, waited on her.

Her love for David made her more sharply aware of her own unhappy fate, and she wept in secret. At such times she sought Jonathan's company all the more eagerly because he spoke to her of his friend and because he praised him and defended him against the accusations of her father and sister.

But when Saul broke his promise to David, and gave Merob to Hadriel of Molathite, Michol sparkled with joy. Her love found expression not as a burning passion but as pity for the man so insulted. The veil of justice cloaked the honor of the enamored girl better than modesty. Since David had been unjustly rejected, Michol would heal that insult with her affection.

Meanwhile, Saul had twice attempted to pin David to the wall with his spear. The king was never without his spear, emblem of royalty. From its inception the monarchy of Israel had differed, even in symbols, from the history of the chosen people, till then led and supported by the shepherd's crook. The staff, an aid in travel, a support in weariness, a rod of punishment, a guide, had always been the symbol of the shepherd. With his staff Moses led his people, and with his staff he won the first battles in the conquest of the Promised Land. Against the Amalechites he raised his staff on high. When he was weary and lowered his arms, the Hebrews fell back before the enemy; when he held up the pastoral rod again, the Amalechites lost ground. Whereupon, he was made to sit down on a stone and Aaron, on one side, and Hur on the other, held up his arms, weary and drained of blood, until the battle was won.

The staff had been the scepter of authority. Its name alone was a synonym for tribe or leader. But Saul, instead, always kept his spear at his side, even when at table. Even in sleep he kept it close at hand, particularly in camp, in his tent. With one blow he thrust it into the ground and laid himself down beside it.

Bending over his harp, David sought the notes among the ten parallel strings and Saul, seized with a desire to kill him as he bent over in concentration, drew near. Restless images passed to and fro through his unstable mind. He saw David in Jonathan's clothes, and Jonathan in David's clothes. His son had divested himself of all outward signs of royalty to give them to his friend. In that substitution of clothes Saul saw another and more odious substitution: he saw David on the throne and Jonathan, at his feet, less than the harpist.

The images of his son and of the usurper mingled in a continuous suspicion of double-dealing. Now it was David and now Jonathan; at one moment Jonathan became David and the next, David blotted out the vision of Jonathan. To put a stop to that perpetual game of substitution, to fix one single image, even if in cruelty and in fear of death, Saul struck with his spear.

Swift as a vision, fleeting as a dream, David vanished. When Saul woke from his madness, the spear still quivered on the ground and the king was alone in the silence.

Far from the circle of hate traced by the royal spear, David was solaced by the healing love of Michol and Jonathan.

It was reported to the king that Michol loved David. He thought: "She will be a trap for him."

Hebrew shepherds never slew wild beasts with weapons. They laid traps for them. Near springs or beside a lamb tied to a stake they dug a ditch and covered it over with grass and twigs. Deceived by the smooth ground, the animals plunged of their own weight, into the ditch.

Saul planned to snare David like a wild beast. Michol, softer than meadow grass, more flexible than willow boughs, more passionate than a hind and more docile than a lamb, would be the trap into which David, having escaped the spear, would easily fall.

As the price of the hand of Michol, Saul sent David on a dangerous mission among the Philistines, hoping that he would be killed. But David returned victorious.

The king's family lived on the second floor of the royal palace. Saul, in all his gloomy majesty, occupied the ground floor. Near David and Michol, no doubt, lived Hadriel and Merob. Timid Michol suffered from that close proximity; she suffered from the indifference with which her sister had insulted David, and from the boldness with which David looked at the woman who had been his fiancée.

More and more passionately in love, Michol followed David shyly. She surrounded him with her love, accompanied him with fear and trembling, always in terror of losing him. At court she feared the envy of rivals and the malicious remarks of his enemies. David's restlessness worried her. It seemed as if it were not enough for the son of Jesse to be the son-in-law of the king. At times he was modest and shy, like a shepherd; at others, haughtier than a prince. Strange longings assailed him: now for greater glory, now for a quiet and obscure life.

For a shepherd his position at court was too high; for a prince it had risen too little. He hid his secret in his heart, like a sin and like a privilege. Not even Jonathan could fathom his secret, not even the faithful Michol.

With all the ingenuity of a woman in love she tried to explain her fears: perhaps David was humiliated because he had not been chosen by the king's eldest daughter; perhaps her timid, submissive love failed to fulfill all of the hero's ambitions; perhaps, from the start, David's love had been spent, chilled by a disillusionment he had suffered.

She tried harder than ever to overcome the waves of nostalgia and the doubts of discontent. But David was not nostalgic for his past, nor was he discontented. He longed for that distant and terrible future Samuel had revealed to him in a still, small voice and a whirlwind of prophetic power.

How would he reach the throne? Would he have to betray and sacrifice Jonathan and Michol, the two beings who loved him with complete devotion? And what of Saul, and Merob? Would he be able to snatch the spear from the unhappy king under the haughty eyes of Merob, under Michol's ardent eyes, in the presence of a prostrate Jonathan? When that day came he would be the saddest man on earth. He shrank from the thought of that unhappiness, but he could not imagine a future less cruel. He lived through the uncertain present in terror of that inevitable future.

Of them all, Saul, with the obsessive lucidity of his madness, followed a definite plan: to kill David. With David's death, the knot that love, hate, and fatality had tied would be severed forever.

He entrusted his son-in-law with the most dangerous tasks in the hope "that the hand of the Philistines would fall heavily upon him." But each time David returned with a victory, and as the knot grew tighter and tighter, the need to cut it became ever more urgent.

Then began the persecution within the king's palace. The upper floor of the royal palace lay heavier and heavier on Saul's household. Only at Jonathan's side could David be safe. When he was alone, every curtain concealed an enemy, every corner sheltered a hired ruffian.

Michol lived in terror. She spied and questioned. She begged Merob to confide in her, she begged her father to have pity. She had no one to help her but Jonathan — a weak and not very alert aid. Jonathan still did not believe that his father desired David's death. When he looked at the king's austere and melancholy countenance, he was assailed by an invincible pity for the bewildered old madman. His affection was a staff for Saul. But the paternal rages disheartened and alienated the son. At such times he would run back to his friend and to his sister, discouraged and dismayed.

One day, in one of his mad rages, Saul ordered Jonathan and his servants to kill David. Jonathan hastened to warn David of the danger. Begging him not to take any chances, he made him hide. And he promised David that he would calm the king's wrath.

Leaving to Michol the task of watching over her husband, he went back to his father and all the next morning never stirred from Saul's side. Jonathan talked at length to the King of David, of his deeds and of his goodness. Saul listened absent-mindedly. Then gratitude and forgiveness, confidence and trust began little by little to seep into his mind. Jonathan's words were more persuasive than David's music. Saul was refreshed by them and David was able to appear before him again.

Michol was neither deceived like Jonathan, nor was she confident like David. Living in terror, she had become suspicious and superstitious. She consulted men and spirits; she guarded David with prayers and amulets. Without her husband's knowledge, she had put his living quarters under the protection of Canaanite idols.

She saw her love threatened by everyone. From her father she feared death; from her sister, derision; from her brother, distrust, from her husband, satiety. She scarcely slept and then but lightly; her life was passed between the intrigues of the royal palace and the mysteries of superstition; between low voices that rose from the first floor and light murmurings that floated down from the magic sphere. She picked up every suspicion, every rumor, every warning.

One evening she learned that before dawn the king's guard would invade her apartment and would murder David in his bed. Warning her husband, she forced him to flee through the window. Then, working feverishly, she placed a wooden idol in his bed and tied a goat's skin around its head. When, with the first cool air of dawn, the hired ruffians broke into David's bedchamber, they discovered the puppet Michol had prepared.

Saul, who was already seated on the throne of stone waiting for the foreign disturber of the family to be brought to him dead, saw Michol, with reddened eyes and trembling with emotion, appear between the soldiers.

"Why," he asked her, "hast thou deceived me so and let my enemy go and flee away?"

On hearing that her beloved was now nothing but "the enemy," Michol repressed a groan but she still concealed her passion: "He forced me to, saying: 'Let me go or else I will kill you.' "

Meanwhile, far away in the light of dawn, David sang:

> In the Lord I put my trust:
> How then do you say to my soul:
> Get thee from hence to the mountain like a sparrow?
> For, lo, the wicked have bent their bow;
> They have prepared their arrows in the quiver;
> To shoot in the dark the upright of heart.

As David sang, Jonathan awoke from a restless sleep and stretched himself lazily.

Jonathan wanted to make one more test. When the moon was new, King Saul invited all his captains to Gabaa. For three days in sequence he would eat in their midst. Taciturn, his thick beard pressed against his chest and his hands spread out on the table, scarcely touching a mouthful, he sat with his back against the wall and his spear close at hand. On either side of him were the seats reserved for the two bravest captains in the kingdom: on one side David; on the other Abner.

David was absent from the banquet of the new moon; so to find out what was in Saul's mind, Jonathan had come tactfully to make his excuses. And when the days of the new moon came, alone on the terrace in the moonless night, Michol listened to the loud voices of the soldiers gathered in the royal palace.

Amid a general silence the king took his seat at the table. Abner sat down beside him. No one dared to occupy David's chair, and there was a vacant seat at the board. But, indifferent and detached, Saul gave no sign of noticing David's absence. Not until the second day did he ask why that place was vacant. Jonathan told him: "David asked leave of me earnestly to go to Bethlehem to his brethren."

Saul was troubled. His bloodless lips quivered with rage. Jonathan spoke again, hoping to soothe his father's ire, for Saul was staring at him sullenly.

Suddenly, as he had done with David, Saul seized the spear beside him and hurled it at his son. . . . A cry rang out. Recognizing the sound of the spear as it rebounded, quivering, against the wall, Michol knew that David was condemned.

Jonathan left the table in tears, and for the rest of that day took no more food. Early in the morning he went out from Gabaa and came to a field of dry stubble. To allay suspicion he took arrows and spears with him and a boy to collect them. The young men of the tribe of Benjamin were in the habit of going to that field early every morning to train with weapons, but Jonathan, weak from fasting and exhausted from weeping, had little strength to draw a bow.

He shot an arrow nearby. The boy ran quickly to retrieve it, but as he was bending over, Jonathan shot another and shouted in a loud voice: "The arrow is there farther beyond you."

Those words were intended both for the boy and for David, who was hiding near the field. To the boy they bore no abstruse meaning. But to David they contained a message previously agreed upon: they meant that Saul was still angry with him, and that he should go as far from Gabaa as possible.

Hearing that message, David would have left, but Jonathan wanted to speak to him. So he shot another arrow or two, and then pretending to be tired said to the boy: "Go and bring back the arrows."

When he was alone, he ran to meet David. For a long time the two friends stood there without speaking in grief-stricken silence. What could they say to each other? There was nothing definite to build on. If they spoke of their past life together, they could only sigh; if they spoke of the future, they could only offer dubious promises of loyalty. To each one on that misty morning the world looked gloomy and meaningless. Only the thought of Michol moved the two young men to pity. The sister and the wife: that delicate young girl, who had no thought but that of love. In Jonathan's ears rang the sound of her weeping, the tears of a heartbroken child; and David saw before him her worried face as she leaned from the high window in the royal palace. For Michol remained at court, a stranger and an enemy, to dream of her unhappy love, again to be subjected to her sister's rule and to know real terror in the restless hands of her father.

Through eyes filled with tears David gazed back toward the royal city. The images quivered: the houses seemed to collapse as his tears gushed forth, and trees took on strange shapes seen through his streaming eyes. And in that chaos the vision of a despairing Michol writhed in the flames of the sun as it rose in whirls of light.

At daybreak Jonathan took leave of his friend. David watched him disappearing wearily in the distance with slow, uncertain steps. Then he, too, headed toward the open country, but with a firmer gait.

In the night without a moon no dew had fallen: the leaves of the plants were still curled up from the heat of the preceding day. And in those parched fields, like the fleece which Gideon stretched as a tent on the threshing floor, David was bathed in tears.

DAVID PERSECUTED

They shall return at evening,
And shall suffer hunger like dogs:
And shall go round about the city.

Behold they shall speak with their mouth,
And a sword is in their lips:
But thou, O Lord, shalt laugh at them:

They shall return at evening
And shall suffer hunger like dogs:
And shall go round about the city.

They shall be scattered abroad to eat,
And shall murmur if they be not filled.

THE sun dried the tears on David's face as his scorn of slanderers and informers dried up pity in the fugitive's heart. His eyes turned green, and his slender nose curved down over his bitter mouth. He repeated:

> They shall suffer hunger like dogs:
> They shall return at evening,
> And shall go round about the city.

He spat out the stanzas and cheated his hunger by swallowing the bitterness of the verses again. Absorbed in his rage at injustice, he looked neither to the right nor to the left, nor did he lift his eyes to the mountains, or to the heavens. Even the sorrow of parting and his longing for home had passed. Only the inner gnawing of rancor remained to accompany him on his way.

The sun was now high in the sky and shadows showed plainly at the traveler's feet. In that uncompromising light objects took on an almost merciless aspect, and David's heart was bitter. Michol was only a small, motionless image in his mind — if she had not vanished altogether. By now the proudest memories of his life at the royal palace were overshadowed by the hardships and bitterness of his journey.

Saul would not have turned against David with such fury in his madness if the king's heart had not been poisoned by jealousy day after day and his suspicions kept alive by the libels of men envious of the good fortune of the shepherd who had become the king's son-in-law.

The Bible has left us the names of only two honest men at Saul's side: David and Abner. One of them sat at the right hand of the king, the other at his left. Was David referring to Abner when he sang those embittered, resentful verses?

But Abner, an honest captain loyal to his king, and an

honorable rival of David, did not deserve the sting of the Davidian invective. He was also a good man and in addition he could not hope to aspire to the throne. The command of the army was enough for him and this he would have held even with David as king. If he felt any dislike for David, it was the legitimate dislike of the soldier for the innovator and troublemaker.

Not against Abner did David turn his curses. Abner, the soldier, fought with the sword; and David, with lips narrowed, eyes clouded, and his mind grim, was not thinking of honorable enemies, but of those men who compensate for their impotence and lack of ability by defaming others. They did not fight like Abner in the service of the king, but in the service of their own little passions they stirred up conflicts and battles.

> They plot iniquity in their hearts
> And every day they stir up dissension.

They stirred up dissension, but they did not fight, for they were secret instigators, careful to remain in the background and not to be drawn into the struggle. David's enemies lurked in the shadows: courtiers and servants, envious of his glory, not emulators of his heroism. David did not even know their faces. He remembered only their tongues as lively as whips, and their lips as sharp as swords.

> All the day long thy tongue hath devised injustice:
> As a sharp razor, thou hast wrought deceit. . . .
> Thou hast loved all the words of ruin,
> O deceitful tongue.

Hungry and tired, David blamed the envenomed tongues of vile men for his downfall and his sufferings.

Force he had fought and conquered; but against slander and recrimination he could not win. Slander was perpetual war, the indomitable rebellion, the poison that spread throughout the world contaminating every source of happiness in it.

Blood invigorates the earth, sweat fecundates it, tears purify it, but the slaver of a scandalmonger contaminates and infects like the worst of poisons.

David arrived at Nobe starving, and remembering his anointing and Samuel's kindness to him, he hastened to the sanctuary.

"Thou shalt set upon the tables the loaves of proposition," says the Law. Unleavened bread was kept hot on the table and renewed every day. Removed and stale, it could be eaten only by the priests.

Achimelech had no other bread but the loaves of proposition and he gave them to David willingly. When David's hunger was satisfied, he felt strong again and he asked for a weapon. In his flight he had brought with him neither sword nor spear, and Jonathan, who had sent the groom back home, had been left without arms.

Achimelech then remembered what David already knew: in the tabernacle, wrapped in a flag, stood Goliath's sword which David himself had consecrated to God after his victory over the giant.

"Give it to me," said David; "there is none like that."

With his own hands Achimelech lifted it from the tabernacle and held it out to Samuel's favorite. David stared at the sword, which twisted unexpectedly in his hand. When Goliath, wounded on the forehead, let fall that sword, David had been nothing but a shepherd. Now, when

Achimelech placed it in his hands again, he was nothing but a fugitive.

Wrapped in cloth, the blade had retained the gloss of steel tempered by the Philistines. Not a scratch or spot of rust marred its mirrorlike surface.

And in that moment it seemed to David that he had set out on his true path again. That troubled period in the royal palace vanished as if it had never been. He was again the conqueror of Goliath. Rivalry and slander, rancor and subterfuges, traps and vengeance faded into nothing. Even Saul and his gloomy madness; even Jonathan and his spasmodic melancholy; even Michol and her passion, all slipped away from him. He was the anointed of God, the conqueror of Goliath, the favorite of Samuel. He flung back his head, shaking his curls. His eyes, so sullen a moment ago, now shone with their usual serene light. He smiled, and again a voice spoke to him those words of mysterious portent: "Thou shalt be King."

Two leagues from Bethlehem, two leagues from David's house, yawned a vast cave. David had known it as a boy when he led his sheep, steaming with dampness, to shelter there during sudden storms.

The entrance was hidden by weeds and difficult to reach because of stones, but once past the opening, the cave widened out to form an empty space large enough to shelter many men and animals crowded together. Toward this cave David fled for refuge from Saul's people.

On the hillside, covered with fruit trees dripping water from every branch, stood Bethlehem, half-hidden in misty low-lying clouds, flooded by countless streams, yellowed and muddied by the continual rains of the season. Fields laid waste and untilled, sheep drenched with rain, and roads that were running torrents had long since forgotten the warmth of the sun. The inhabitants had withdrawn into the city, where they crowded like ants around the granaries. Seldom did anyone climb up over the hill, driving before him a heavily laden donkey.

David would have dearly loved to walk through those familiar city streets, to enter his father's house and embrace his brothers again. He would have smelled the warm, heavy odor of sheep huddled close together in the stable and have heard the lambs' bleat as they nuzzled against the wool of the mother sheep.

But the sight of that waterlogged city brought David scarcely a twinge of nostalgia. He felt Goliath's sword pressing against his flank; and instead of going up toward the hill of Bethlehem, he turned off resolutely toward the dark entrance to the cave of Odollam.

Once inside, his nostrils were assailed by a pungent, earthy odor. The close, motionless air was damp. As he searched in the dark for a place to sit down, several drops of water fell on his neck. He shivered and moved back to the opening. Framed in the dark arch of the entrance, earth and sky appeared, washed clean by the rain.

He thought of his life when he was a shepherd and the paths he had traveled with his flocks: "Make me to know Thy ways, O Lord." He thought again of those lonely mountain paths, worn by streams, cluttered with stones rolled down by the torrents, and choked with innumerable weeds and sandy islets. Hill paths, easy roads furrowed in circles, with a hedge above and an escarpment below. Level roads, light glades, with trails branching out in all directions. Roads over which a flock passed for the first time, scarcely bruising the soft sward of the meadow with their hoofs.

In his sadness David let his thoughts be drawn back nostalgically over those roads. On a high cliff some tufts of grass, touched by the light, bent and waved in the wind, scattering drops of water like tears.

At nightfall David's seven brothers came out from their house bringing bread and toasted barley. They walked in silence as far as the cave of Odollam. In the rain-drenched sky, dark clouds, driven by the wind, scurried past to break apart against the silvery moon, and the thoughts of the seven brothers were just as dark, and scattered as they considered the news of David's arrival in the neighborhood of Bethlehem.

The presence of that adventurous brother made a sudden change in their lives. Like all farmers, they disliked novelty and change. They had served the king as soldiers when David was still a shepherd and more than once their father had sent the younger brother to their camp with provisions of bread and toasted barley. Now they were doing the same for that brother; but as they passed along the road, amid flashes of light that shone on fresh pools of water, they were already wishing themselves on their way back home.

When they came to the cave, David barely recognized them. Eliab, the tallest, whom Samuel had thought very handsome, already stooped from the shoulders. Abinadai and Samma spoke rarely and then in sullen tones, like men who no longer expect an answer to their deep and innermost thoughts. Even the last four, though younger, now felt that they belonged to an older generation. They remembered the first wars against the Philistines, as they would look back upon a far-distant youth. No thought of adventure or glory ever crossed their minds.

They seated themselves in a circle, at the edge of the cave, and the shadow made by their heads fell between their outspread knees. They were men of few words. They did not disown their brother, but his arrival in Bethlehem was a threat to their fields and their granaries. Saul would not miss this opportunity to lay hands on the tribe of Juda that harbored his rival. The seven brothers expressed their fears with that thoughtful air that veils reproach but makes it all the more impressive. When they fell silent, David looked at their shadows, deformed and unrecognizable against the curved walls of the cave. Then he saw them walk away, a silent cortege along the hilly road, between dark growths of vegetation and broad, open spaces of moonlight.

The next day, in the early morning with its rich fresh colors and its air that carried voices clearly, David's nephews arrived at the cave. They were his sister's sons — that sister who had grown up with David and, like him, was fearless and full of life. Her name was Sarvia and she herself led her sons up the washed and shining slope. Rather, she led her sons with her voice the way one drives fast horses on the rein; for Joab, Abisai, and Asael hurried ahead of her along the road, impatient to reach their uncle's dwelling place.

Ever since childhood Sarvia's sons had heard stories about that maternal uncle. They knew his life like a book — and his victory over Goliath, his marriage with the king's daughter, had fired their youthful imaginations. When they heard that David was hiding in their country, there was no holding them back. They would have joined their uncles had they not been repelled by the latters' caution. They would have searched the whole countryside — and aroused general suspicion in the doing —

had their mother not relented and set out to show them the way.

They were peering eagerly into the dark cave when suddenly David stood in the entrance. He was pale and wan in the early light of dawn after a sleepless night. Their eyes took in at once the flaming hair, the seductive mouth, the fascinating eyes, the sword at his side, as David turned and smiled sadly at his beloved sister.

When he had embraced Sarvia, he turned his steady gaze on his awestruck nephews. They looked younger than he, but of the same generation. Between uncle and nephews there was just that difference in age which makes leaders and plain soldiers contemporaries and fit for the same enterprise. David's lean, slender body, with its beautifully co-ordinated muscles, was still as supple as a young boy's. Joab, on the other hand, was short and heavy-set, firmly planted on two stubby bowed legs, with a head like a lion's mane set on two broad shoulders. When he smiled, his whole face wrinkled in a sort of ferocious glee and his strong, sharp teeth clamped down over full, fleshy lips like an ivory clasp on satin. Abisai stood a shoulder above him. Not so strong, but craftier. More the hyena than the lion, Asael, the youngest, had outgrown both of his brothers. Thin, slender, with large eyes and a pointed face, he looked like a wild gazelle. An extremely swift runner, he never knew fatigue or thirst and could march all day across the desert on one drink of water.

These were Sarvia's sons. She showed them to David, described their natures and capabilities, and offered them to her brother that he might put them to the test. And the three youths shuffled their feet restlessly, eager for the fray.

Thus a steady stream of relatives and acquaintances began to flow between the cave of Odollam and "the house of bread." David's old parents went down from Bethlehem. His brothers came back several times. Restless spirits, men who loved adventure, gathered around him.

"All that were in distress," says the Book of Kings, "and oppressed with debt, and under affliction of mind."

Some of the men were disoriented and trying to find themselves; one man plotted revenge, another to avenge an insult; and some came because they could not pay their debts. Young men, especially, who saw in David heroism and adventure, came down from Bethlehem to join the son-in-law of the king, the fugitive from the royal palace.

With David as their leader, four hundred men crowded into the cave of Odollam, where they lived like ants. In the morning they filed out through the narrow opening and scattered over the land of bread. Not a man of them neglected his barley and wheat, his kids and lambs. The cave became a cross between a fortress and a granary. But of one thing they were all aware: Saul would not permit such a large gathering of men in the heart of Juda. David realized that his life as a guerrilla leader would not last very long if he let himself be driven out of the cave, or, as was more probable, trapped there. So he moved his four hundred men out from the cave and, leaving Juda, crossed the desert and headed toward the devastated country of Ruth.

Nor did he tarry there long, for the prophet Gad warned him: "Abide not in the hold, depart and go into the land of Juda."

David's recall into Israel had been the priest's secret

challenge to Saul. Blinded by rage and madness, the king answered that defiance by murdering Achimelech.

At Nobe a certain Doeg had been present in the sanctuary when Achimelech fed the king's son-in-law and armed him with the sword of Goliath. This man reported everything to Saul.

Now one form of scandalmongering consists of telling only half the truth. Doeg reported truthfully that Achimelech had fed David unleavened bread and had given him Goliath's sword, but he did not say that David had concealed from the high priest the fact that he was a fugitive.

Saul, who saw traitors and allies of David on every hand, summoned Achimelech before him. The high priest did not deny what he had done. He was put to death and with him his family and all the inhabitants of Nobe — men, women, and babes at the breast. Even the oxen, the asses, and the sheep were destroyed by the sword of Saul.

But as always happened in his excesses of madness, after that wholesale slaughter Saul felt lonelier and more in danger than ever in the tragic silence wrought by his own sword and spear. There was an undefinable something he could not grasp, something that escaped like a live bird from his trembling hands.

This time it was Abiathar, Achimelech's last son, who, fleeing the massacre, turned up among the men around Jesse's youngest son and placed himself behind the holy efod. By breaking through Saul's net and allying himself with the youthful branch of the tribe of Juda, Abiathar brought good luck to David and a sinister warning to Saul.

Up to now David's company had been merely a gang of fugitives and rebels. Every good Israelite, particularly every loyal soldier, had felt impelled to fight against that handful of rebels, led by a rabble-rouser. By fleeing from the hands of Saul, Abiathar gave the leader of those rebels authority and respect for religion. By his presence he made the revolution lawful. If the last of the race of high priests could live only when defended by David's arms, those arms could not be sacrilegious.

Realizing the significance of that event, David proclaimed himself defender of Israel and of the religion of the chosen people. When he learned that the Philistines had returned to Ceila and were sacking the barns, he hastened to liberate the city. His enjoyment of his victory was short-lived, for Saul, angered by David's boldness and even more because he himself had reached the threshing floors of Ceilia too late, surrounded the city with a vast number of armed men.

David escaped from this trap with difficulty. His nephews, who comprised the more belligerent nucleus of his followers, thrust forward in a wedge against the circle of Saul's army and opened a breach toward the mountains. Boldly and impudently they marched ahead of David, destroying obstacles in the way, cutting a path through the woods. Asael, swifter and nimbler than the others, scouted ahead of his brothers while Abisai and Joab went back and forth beside him, offering opposition equally with their shoulders and their swords. When they met resistance, Asael gave ground and the stronger Joab attacked the enemy.

With the slower and larger part of the army David sought refuge in the woods, but not even in that shade speckled with sunlight did he feel secure. He withdrew toward the desert, but Saul's men pursued him stubbornly even across the desert.

With a few specially picked men, he wormed his way

up through the bare trees and impenetrable mountains, but Saul did not slow down the chase. For David had publicly usurped the functions of a king and Saul was determined to punish him with death.

Michol now belonged to someone else. Jonathan had met David for the last time in the woods and renewed his vows of friendship, but the prince no longer had a voice in his father's council.

Saul had placed his sole trust in Abner's military skill, and Abner led the army shrewdly and tenaciously. David's enemies were closing in upon him. No human aid could save him now. Even Joab's face was glum. No longer did he exhibit that concentrated will to tear and wound. Abisai showed signs of dejection, Asael of weariness.

In those moments David alone appeared invincible. Hope, nourished by prayer, lighted his weary countenance:

> In thee, O Lord, have I hoped,
> Let me never be confounded.
>
> Have mercy on me, O Lord, for I am afflicted:
> My eye is troubled with wrath,
> My soul and my belly:
>
> For my life is wasted with grief:
> And my years in sighs.
> My strength is weakened through poverty
> And my bones are disturbed.
>
> But I have put my trust in thee, O Lord:
> I said: Thou art my God.
> My lots are in thy hands.
> Deliver me out of the hands of my enemies.
>
> Into thy hands I commend my spirit:
> Thou hast redeemed me, O Lord,
> The God of truth.

Just as Saul was about to capture David, a messenger arrived saying to the king: "Come, the Philistines are in the land."

Abandoning pursuit, Saul returned home to fight the Philistines. But when he had driven out the enemy, he set forth again after David, determined to follow him even among craggy rocks where only the chamois could find a foothold.

David now left the lands of Juda forever and, for safety's sake, withdrew to the most desolate and inaccessible part of Palestine. A few leagues from Bethlehem and Hebron, toward the west, lies a region the Hebrews called "the land of desolation." At first a monotonous succession of low, arid hills covered with green underbrush and yellow broom, the farther one goes, the poorer the land becomes. Broom gives way to thistles, then even the thistles become rare, and the sun beats down on a yellowish chalky sand deeply ridged by dried watercourses made by windstorms. Here and there, between the shining sands, the tops of white rocks appear as if the earth, worn thin, were displaying its ribs shrunken and bleached by the burning sun.

The sky here is almost always clear and cruelly bright. But when the clouds gather, rain pours down with a terrifying violence and roar. Then the ridges sink, the sand is swept away, and the whole land moves as if caught in a whirlpool toward the lake just visible through a gap in the vast chalky basin in which it lies. Near that immense, placid lake, which rests in its long, narrow basin as in a bed, the land seems to come to life again, almost as if the air from that great tranquil sheet of water were about to give birth to vegetation again. The illusion does not last long. In that clear air all the troughs and waves on the lake are plainly visible, but there is not a sign of life. Crows and vultures hover over that blue expanse of deep water as over a grave, feeding on fish carried there by rivers to die in those lethal waters.

It is the lake of ill-omen, known to the Hebrews as the Salt Sea. Later, the Greeks called it the Sea of Asphalt; the Latins, the Dead Sea, and the Arabs, the Sea of Lot. When the divine fire reduced Sodom and Gomorrah to ashes, the waters of that lake swept down and inundated the valley. Abraham bore witness that he saw columns of burning fire descend from heaven on the city of Lot.

To that desolate region David led his men and there encamped. A pursuing army would have ventured with difficulty among those rocky peaks and sandy valleys. Now and then in the midst of so much barren waste one came upon an oasis, like Engaddi, where palm trees flourished, acacias flowered, delicate fragrances perfumed the air, and brilliant colors delighted the eye.

However, David and his men did not dwell in those oases, neither did they live on their delicious fruits. Instead, he was forced to hide again in caves in the most inaccessible places, and again depended upon native flocks for sustenance. For if, at first glance, the land looked to be uninhabited, as they penetrated farther into the interior David and his men saw large flocks of thin, stunted sheep browsing contentedly among stiff tufts of broom or on spiny tops of thistles, or where a ragged line of grass barely showed above the ground. Their wool was as tight and harsh as the thistle; their milk as yellow as clay; yet in that desert they were the only sign of wealth and prosperity. And they were easy prey for Iduminean and Moabite thieves.

By his presence David held those thieves at bay. The flocks were safe, and twice a year their owners rounded them up and celebrated the feast of shearing. Curls of wool fell under the shears, intoxicating the shepherds with their strong, wild odor so that, during that time, especially if the shearing was large, the men caroused and made merry. They ate their fill then, exhilarated by the wine, lay down to sleep on clear nights beside their sheep; and the poor animals shivered in their nakedness after the shears had done their work.

At such times David appeared at the sheepfolds and demanded compensation for the watch his men had kept over the flocks. And not a single man refused him wool, lambs, and dairy products, for he made his request with his sword at his side and his bow thrown over his shoulders.

Nabel had gathered together three thousand lambs and a thousand goats for the shearing, and his wife Abigail had prepared the food for the ceremonial banquet: bread baked under the ashes, roast ram, toasted corn, dried figs, and bunches of grapes. Wine in goatskin flasks and small jars of honey perfumed the supply tent, which had been decorated with myrtle and juniper. Laughing and talking merrily, the shepherds were busy rolling flocks of wool into balls, which were then tied up and painted with numbers and initials, when ten young men from David's army appeared on the threshing floor.

"Peace be to my brethren and to thee, and peace to thy house and peace to all thou hast," they said to Nabal, who was eyeing them suspiciously. "David has heard that thy shepherds are shearing. He has never molested you and has guarded thy flocks. Ask thy servants whether there was aught missing of the flock at any time. We are come in a good day. David asks that you send him whatsoever you desire and whatsoever thy hand shall find."

Now this message angered Nabal, and, knowing that he had a hundred or more big, strong young men behind him, perhaps, too, because his good fortune had gone to his head, he drew himself up haughtily.

"And who is this David?" he asked sarcastically. "Servants are multiplied nowadays who flee from their masters."

When he was told this reply, David said to his comrades: "Let every man gird on his sword."

Joab, Abisai, Asael, and the whole company leapt to arms so eagerly that David had the greatest difficulty in restraining their lust for blood. Seldom did he give an order to arm, for he was ever inclined to moderation. But this time, seeing him pale with rage, his eyes flaming with visions of swift revenge, his men were seized with a passionate desire for action. Tense and impatient, they milled around him, holding their breath and restraining their fierce joy at the coming slaughter. David set out and four hundred men followed after him more gaily than guests at Nabal's banquet.

When Abigail heard that David was approaching with his men, she realized that by evening there would not be a man left on his feet, or a woman who had not been violated, or a lamb alive on her husband's threshing floors and sheepfolds. Hurrying to the pantry she took two hundred loaves of bread, two goatskins of wine, five roast kids, five measures of toasted corn, one hundred bunches of grapes and two hundred bundles of dried figs. All this she loaded on two asses; then putting on fresh garments, she brushed her hair and, draping a richly woven veil over her head, mounted a white she-ass. Saying nothing to her husband, Abigail rode out to meet the band of outlaws.

David climbed up a narrow trail between rocks cracked by the heat of the sun, a climb made more difficult by his anger and shortness of breath. A mist of blood obscured his sight.

As he rounded a turn in the road, Abigail appeared before him like a vision. Dismounting from the ass, the woman came to meet him and prostrated herself at his feet.

"Let thy handmaid speak and hear the words of thy servant."

David was abashed by that humble attitude. He did not understand what the woman wanted of him.

"Give no heed to the words of Nabal," Abigail implored; "for, according to his name, he is a fool. But I, thy handmaid, did not see thy servants."

David realized why the woman had intervened. But his men were crowding at his back. Unmoved by her words, they would gladly have trampled over that prostrate veiled figure had Abigail not risen and, as if divining their greed for plunder, run to the asses crying:

"Receive this blessing which thy handmaid hath brought to thee, my lord; and give it to the young men that follow thee. Forgive the iniquity of thy handmaid; for the Lord will surely make for my lord a faithful house, because thou fightest the battles of the Lord thy God; let not evil therefore be found in thee all the days of thy life. If any man at any time shall arise and persecute thee and seek thy life, the soul of my lord shall be kept with the Lord thy God; but the souls of thy enemies shall be whirled as with the violence and whirling of a sling. When then the Lord shall have done to thee all the good that He hath spoken concerning thee and shall have made thee prince over Israel, this shall not be an occasion of grief to thee, and a scruple of heart to my lord that thou hast shed innocent blood or hast revenged thyself. And when the Lord shall have done well by my lord, thou shalt remember thy handmaid. Selah."

Abigail's head rested in the dust of the road. The veil trembled over her prostrate, agitated body. David was amazed at the woman's action and enchanted by the sound of her words. And peace began to descend on him again. His eyes under his frowning brows became clearer and bluer than a lake.

Subtly Abigail played on all the strings that stirred sad but sweet memories in the young hero. She spoke to the banished man of "those who meditate evil." She wished the wanderer, deprived of parents, wife and home, "a faithful house." She reminded the hero of "the battles of the Lord," referred casually, and therefore with more subtle emphasis, to the "whirling sling." Not to him did she offer her gifts but to the young men who followed him; to him she offered peace of mind: "This shall not be an occasion of grief to thee, and a scruple of heart to my lord, that thou hast shed innocent blood."

She, the wife of the "fool," the woman raised among shepherds and merchants, had understood David's generous nature better than the princesses of the blood royal. He did not feel that he was a rebel or a traitor; much less a thief or blackmailer. "I am," he said in his canticles, "as a fruitful olive tree." Peace of mind he sought, nor did he desire to find evil all the days of his life. And finally he felt that if he was faithful to his trust the Lord would do well by him as He had promised.

Abigail's words raised his thoughts above passion and

hate and he was lost in meditation. At last he spoke, and his voice was warm and human.

"Blessed be the Lord, the God of Israel, Who sent thee this day to meet me, and blessed be thy speech which has kept me today from coming to blood and revenging me with my own hand."

He accepted her gifts. Then, reassuring the woman, he sent her back and commanded his disappointed comrades to sheathe their swords and return, without bloodshed, to their caves in the mountain.

Saul's mad desire to punish David drove him to the top of Engaddi, with three thousand men-at-arms. But he was getting old now, heavy and slow in body, and his mind was clouded, and twice he fell into David's hands.

The first time was in a mountain cave, much like the cave of Odollam, narrow at the entrance and wide within. David and his men were hidden at the back of the cave when Saul entered, in need of rest and refreshment. The eyes of Joab, Abisai, Asael, and all the other comrades glittered with a cruel light in the dusky cavern. And they said to David: "God hath shut up thy enemy this day into thy hands."

But David would not raise a hand against the king. All he did was to cut off the hem of Saul's robe in proof of his devotion.

And after Saul had arisen and gone out of the cave, David stood at the entrance and waved the piece of garment he had cut off to show the king that he had had him in his hands and had respected him. That day Saul was obliged to admit that David was more just than he.

The second time, seeing the place in a woods where

the royal tent was pitched, David said to his nephews:

"Who will go down with me tonight to Saul into the camp?"

Abisai was quicker than the others to offer himself, and during the night uncle and nephew came to the tent where Saul and his captains slept. They found the king asleep, his spear fixed in the ground at his head. Wearied from the day's pursuit, Abner and Saul's other captains lay sleeping around him.

For a moment David stood and gazed at the majestic figure of the old king, so placid in sleep. Abisai bared his teeth like a hyena.

"I will run him through with my spear even to the earth at once," he whispered "and there shall be no need of a second time."

He was already tasting the joy of that blow straight to the heart. The king would not even have moved; he would not even have uttered a groan. Only a trickle of bloody saliva would have dribbled down from his lips over his beard.

David grasped the raised arm: "Take the spear which is at his head," he said, "and the cup of water and let us go."

Then, taking the spear and the cup of water, they went away. The branches in that oak woods looked like hammered iron, hard outlines of leaves showing black against the dim, moonlit sky. In that great silence even the shadows were motionless. David and Abisai passed through the dark foliage and no one heard them. And when they had come up on a height above a broad plain they stopped and David called Abner in a loud voice. The echo roused the night.

Abner awoke with a start and with him all the camp.

"Who art thou that criest and disturbest the king?" Abner asked.

In a voice that sang like a spring of water David called ironically: "Why, then, hast thou not kept the lord thy king? And now where is the king's spear and the cup of water which was at his head?"

Saul recognized David's voice. Rising on his elbow he looked around him. His spear had vanished; the cup of water from which he had drunk was no longer there. He shivered, chilled by the damp ground and his interrupted sleep.

And Saul bowed his head sorrowfully, but around him rose confused murmurs of anger and hatred against David as he spoke his last farewell to the jealous king:

"If the Lord stir thee up against me, let Him accept of sacrifice: but if the sons of men drive thee to hate me, they are cursed in the sight of the Lord, who have cast me out this day, that I should not dwell in the inheritance of the Lord, saying: Go, serve strange gods."

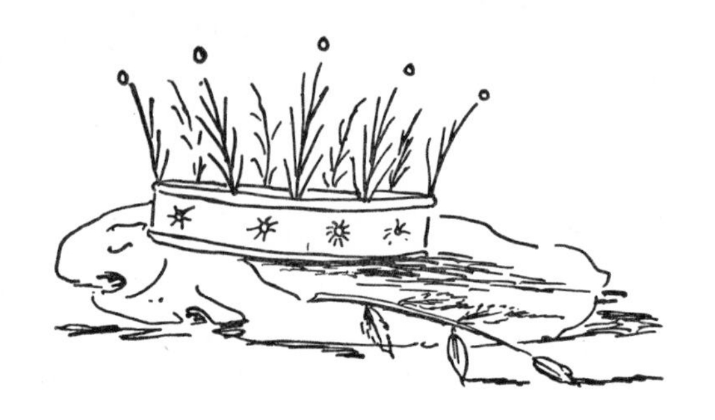

DAVID, KING OF JUDA

THERE appeared to David a messenger from the Amalechites, with his garments torn and dust strewn upon his head. And when he came to David he fell upon his face before him, saying that Saul and Jonathan were dead, slain by the Philistines in the battle of Gelboe. He himself, an Amalechite, had killed the king. And he showed David the diadem and the bracelets.

"I killed him, for I knew that he could not live after the fall; and I took the diadem that was on his head and the bracelet that was on his arm, and have brought them hither to thee, my lord."

"Why didst thou not fear to put out thy hand to kill the Lord's anointed?" David said to him. And he ordered the messenger of death put to death.

David's first act, three days after Saul's death, was in defense of royalty. For three days the body of Saul, slain on Mount Gelboe, hung, headless, from the walls of Bethsan. For three days the throne of stone was empty at Gabaa, but royalty still sat upon it.

Royalty survived Saul's mortal body; it was a twin soul that made the king immortal. Out of respect for royalty, David had twice spared the life of his enemy. In his devotion to royalty, he had put to death the Amalechite who had dared to stretch out his hand against a defeated Saul.

Pursued in the desert or surrounded in the woods, David had never asked God to slay his persecutor. "Free me of mine enemies." . . . "Confound them." . . . "Let them be caught in their own traps." Throughout all his persecution he had never cursed the king. "Thou shalt not speak against a prince of thy people," says the Mosaic law.

David cursed slanderers; raged against informers; scorned liars. But no curses or reproofs for Saul the jealous and ungenerous. In his battles against Saul, David always fought at a disadvantage. Persecuted, he could not persecute; pursued, he could not pursue; beaten, he could not strike back; in constant danger of death himself, he could not threaten his rival with death.

The Greeks portrayed their heroes as struggling against blind fate. David fought against a rival twice hallowed, by madness and by the crown. He felt that his glory lay in being humble, and never once did he make the mistake of putting himself on an equal with Saul.

Sarvia's sons and David's companions did not understand why their leader persisted in keeping them in that equivocal state of rebels faithful to the king and outlaws subject to the duties of citizens. On the other hand, that apparent contradiction, that unwillingness to use his power, that inward struggle of David's between respect and arrogance, between love and pride, were of the essence of their leader's mysterious fascination.

If Samuel had told Joab he would inherit a kingdom, that son of Sarvia would have flung himself upon the throne, savagely drenching the steps to it in blood. But David waited for the most unusual and richest paths to be opened up before him and was amazed to discover the Lord's designs throughout his life. Never did he let desire interfere with grace, but, as in the practice of art, sought through inspiration more felicitous ways to attain his ends.

The Amalechite messenger sold his wretched life for a song, for it was not true that he had slain his king. Saul had been wounded, and to save himself from the hands of the Philistines he had fallen upon his own sword.

At the end of the day Saul had emerged from his tent to watch the sunset. There was a reddish glow in the west and a pale sky in the east. As the shadows vanished, darkness settled down, exaggerating the size of objects. Only the bare ridges on the horizon stood out against the sky in strange and unexpected outlines.

Every evening the old king watched in terror as night fell over the world, for night had long since ceased to bring him rest or peace. The mystery he kept closed up in his heart all day as in a fist, expanded at night. There was no longer any need for Saul to shield his heart from the light and from those near him. The dark dissolved that clot of mystery which by day had been as grateful to him as shadows at noontide, and night with all its terrors entered his heart.

At daybreak sleep overcame him and in the few hours' rest the walls of night fell. When he awoke his withered heart held only the usual shadow of anguish in its tired hand.

The moon had not yet risen over the heights of Gelboe. In the silent camp the slightest noise aroused prolonged echoes. Saul had watched until the last shimmer of light was spent. The stars, far, far away and cold, came out in the sky.

The day was done, night held sway, but soon it, too, would be vanquished and the world filled with the new day. What did that day hold in store for the bemused king? In a few short hours new events would unfold like flowers; and Saul wavered between his longing to pierce that mystery and his fear of it.

At dawn he would meet the Philistines in the most dangerous battle he had yet waged. His enemies, encamped opposite him, were as numerous as the sands of the sea, and as hard as iron. What fate awaited him? The soldier's courage wavered. In that supreme moment the warrior revealed his fatal weaknesses.

No one needed supernatural aid more than he, Samuel's antagonist and Achimelech's murderer. A "voice" would have been enough; but the night brooded in silence. A "sign" would have sufficed; but the stars twinkled in their perpetual luminous oscillation. Not a seer, not a priest, not a prophet of the Lord at the side of that desperate king; only silence and the brutal indifference of soldiers sleeping off their fatigue.

At that moment he remembered his early years when Samuel had been his guide. Samuel "saw," conquered the dark, lighted the path of the young king. In those days Saul had walked as if on the sharp blade of his own sword. He had been as serene as Abner lying there fast asleep with his head cradled on his arm. Samuel took upon himself the burden of the nights and the anxiety of vigils. In those days Saul could sleep till dawn, when, refreshed, he would go forth to battle like the sun coming out from behind the clouds.

He felt a great desire to hear Samuel's voice again. Samuel, the seer, could look into endless time. During his lifetime he had foretold more than one event to the king. Dead he should be even better able to foresee the future.

Since the day when he tore the prophet's cloak, Saul had not seen Samuel again. The seer was dead when David fled before a relentless Saul. In the folly of his madness Saul thought it would be easier to evoke a dead man than to call back a living one.

He questioned his servants: did they know of a woman who had the power of divination? The servants trembled at his words. They knew that Saul had exterminated all the sorcerers and necromancers in the land. At first on Samuel's advice, then out of jealousy and in fear of spells and sortilege, he had mercilessly persecuted the diviners and the pythonesses. In all Israel there was only one woman left capable of sorcery and sortilege, and she dwelt in hiding on the hill of Endor.

Saul demanded to know where the woman was hidden. Voices ran through the night, gathering information and directions. At length a man was found who could guide the king to the enchantress' hovel.

The night was already well advanced when the king issued forth secretly from camp, garbed as a pilgrim and accompanied by only two men, also plainly dressed.

Crossing the valley between the two armies Saul passed close to the outposts of the Philistines, where tall flames from their fires cast moving shadows round about. Then he groped his way toward the village of Endor. A faint light showed him where the hovels of the village stood. With some difficulty the men found the entrance to the diviner's hut. Saul put his shoulder against the door, it gave way and, covering his face, he went in.

The woman crouched in a corner of the hut trembling with mingled fear and delight. She had heard that someone was approaching her hut, and all evening she had been a prey to agitation and anxiety. In the dark she could feel that restless soul seeking her. Removing the bar from the entrance, she had fled to the back of the hut, to hide behind the fire. Tongues of flame and wisps of smoke whirled before her shining eyes. Her heart pounded wildly as she waited for the man, with his face covered, to speak.

"Bring me up him whom I shall tell thee," Saul commanded.

The woman did not move.

"Why dost thou lay a snare for my life, to cause me to be put to death?"

Saul reassured her. "As the Lord liveth, there shall no evil happen to thee for this thing."

On hearing those words the woman yielded promptly, though more to her own desire than to Saul's plea.

Rising, she approached the stranger, and then only was she aware of the man's imposing height. The cloak Saul held over his face made him appear even taller and the fire, lighting him from below, prolonged his gigantic shadow.

The woman had a suspicion. She tried to smile, but she trembled so violently that she could not open her lips and on her cheeks small star-shaped lines appeared. She was not old, and in her excitement, with her hair drawn back revealing her bare forehead, she could even have been called pretty.

"Whom shall I bring up to thee?" she asked in a faint voice, and lowered her eyes with a show of modesty.

Saul hesitated, then leaning down to her, he said: "Bring me up Samuel." His voice failed him and the last syllables ended in a groan. The woman prostrated herself at the stranger's feet.

"Thou art Saul," she cried, and her body shook with terror. "Thou art Saul. Thou art come to kill me."

But Saul did not even hear her. Bending over her he demanded: "What hast thou seen? What hast thou seen?"

With dilated eyes and teeth chattering from fright, her face white and stony, the terrified woman replied: "I saw a god ascending out of the earth."

Saul plied her with questions: "Of what form is he? How dressed?"

"He is an old man, and he cometh up covered with a white mantle."

Saul prostrated himself.

"Why hast thou disturbed my rest, that I should be brought up?" asked the shade. Saul asked what the outcome of the approaching battle would be.

"Tomorrow," said the old man implacably, "thou and thy sons shall be with me and the Lord will deliver the army of Israel into the hands of the Philistines."

And forthwith Saul fell full length on the ground, for he was frightened at the words of Samuel, and there was no strength in him, for he had eaten no bread all that day.

Now all motherly solicitude, the woman offered bread to the king. He refused it, but as he had not the strength to raise himself, she called in the two men of his escort and they laid the king on her bed. At last he partook of food and insisted upon returning to camp before dawn.

Supported by his guides, Saul descended the hill of Endor, passed again behind the Philistines' sentinels, and crossing the valley, arrived at camp just as the joyous singing of larks heralded the dawn of his last day.

His sons were already armed and waiting for him, worried at his delay. When he saw them, so young and so strong, ready for battle and death, his heart failed him. He wanted to advise them to flee, to save themselves from slaughter. But he could not utter the words. Stripping off the humble garments, he put on his armor and the royal insignia. He felt no regret for that insignia, destined so soon to fall, but his eyes searched his sons' faces eagerly, those sons doomed to die with him. In their end he suffered his own death. All his guilt, all his crimes, he saw again through the eyes of his innocent sons.

Jonathan read his fate in his father's despairing eyes and turned to him with more affection. There was no note of reproach in his voice, no regret in the attitude of joy and confidence he assumed. And all morning long, as the serene eye of day opened, father and son kept up that merciful pretense, each concealing his own presentiment of death, each wearing a false mask of gaiety. When, finally, the trumpets blew and the din of battle rose from the earth like natural signs of life aroused by the sun, the sons took leave of their father almost with relief, and hastened toward release from that anguish that had darkened all their young lives.

Saul watched them, so young and resolute, go out to meet the enemy. His blood, crying out after them, choked him. He saw the first flash of their arms, then they vanished into the thick of the fight from which they did not emerge again. . . .

When the Philistines had thrown back the first Israelite phalanx, they swept down on the camp carrying the full force of their attack against the king's tent. Saul had not moved from his post. The eye that had followed his sons to the very threshold of death had seen the enemy break ranks and advance, but had sent no message of rage or fear to the petrified mind.

Saul watched to see whether any of his sons would return to die at his feet. When he found the Philistines on top of him he had one last impulse to defend himself. Almost unconsciously his body shrank from the death he had desired and experienced in the death of his sons. He shot an arrow at the enemy nearest him and withdrew swiftly toward the top of the mount. But the Philistine archers sighted him. An arrow pierced below his ribs.

Panting, racked with pain, he reached the top of Gelboe wounded in the abdomen. Every breath was exquisite torture. In his agony he thought the sky grew dark, the ground atrociously hard. Pain swept over him, blotting out every other emotion. He begged his armor bearer to put an end to his suffering, but the armor bearer did not have the courage to strike the blow. At that, resting the hilt of his sword on the ground, Saul fell upon his own sword. And the first King of Israel, who when alive stood head and shoulders above all his warriors, lay dead upon the mountain.

David did not put on the diadem nor did he adorn himself with the bracelets; instead, he rent his clothes and fasted until evening. He did not stain his grief with blood, because the law forbids disfigurement of the body. "Nor shall you cut your hair roundwise . . . nor make any cuttings in your flesh for the dead."

In the land of Ruth, when the Moabites mourned their dead, more violent scenes often took place. Men disfigured themselves by shaving half of their head or shaving it in streaks. They pulled out their beards, cut gashes in their hands and in their arms. Tearing their cheeks and their breasts, the women bound their hair to the tombstones.

David had Moabite blood in his veins and his grief was violent. Unable to repress his emotions, he vented his sorrow in bitter weeping. But he controlled his instinct and instead of turning cruel in grief, he sought to release his emotions in song.

Holding his harp against his anguished breast David sang:

Ye mountains of Gelboe, let neither dew,
Nor rain come upon you,
Neither be they fields of fresh fruits:
For there was cast away the shield of the valiant,
The shield of Saul bright with oil no more.

From the blood of the slain,
From the fat of the valiant,
The arrow of Jonathan never turned back,
And the sword of Saul did not return empty.

Saul and Jonathan, lovely and comely . . .
Even in death they were not divided.
They were swifter than eagles,
Stronger than lions.

Ye daughters of Israel, weep over Saul,
Who clothed you with scarlet in delights,
Who gave ornaments of gold for your attire.

How are the valiant fallen in battle? . . .
I grieve for thee, my brother Jonathan,
Exceedingly beautiful, and amiable to me,
Above the love of women . . . so did I love thee.
How are the valiant fallen,
And the weapons of war perished?

The *quinah,* which began with a lament, ended on a warlike shout. As he sang, David thought of Saul and Jonathan and pictured to himself the battlefield, Saul's shield and Jonathan's bow. The "song of lament" became a song of praise of the heroes.

David ended on a ringing note, his eyes flashing. When he stopped singing, he had lost the dejected, half-mad appearance of the mourner. His features hardened in an expression of command. He gave orders that the song of the bow be preserved among the national songs, and that all the young men of Israel sing it.

When he had vented his sorrow and exaltation in song, he turned his thoughts to gathering up and honoring the bodies of those who had fallen on Mount Gelboe. But the citizens of Jabes had already attended to that pitiable task.

Jabes was the first city that had been liberated by Saul. He had been king a month when Naas, King of the Ammonites, threatened that city. The ancients of Jabes asked for peace and a covenant, but Naas replied sarcastically: "On this condition will I make a covenant with you, that I may pluck out all your right eyes, and make you a reproach in all Israel."

Then Saul had ordered the oxen that were harnessed to his plow to be cut into pieces, and sending the pieces to all the tribes, he had made his first declaration of war: "Whosoever shall not come forth, and follow Saul and

Samuel to liberate Jabes, so shall it be done to his oxen."

The citizens had never forgotten Saul's gesture, and when they learned that the body of their former liberator hung from the wall of Bethsan, they went out by night and, defying the Philistines' guards, cut it down secretly. The head and the arms of the first King of Israel held aloft on a pike made a sad trophy in the temple of Astaroth, but the inhabitants of Jabes took Saul's decapitated body, burned it with perfume, and buried the ashes in the woods of Jabes.

David sent messengers to Jabes and blessed the inhabitants, who had shown such respect to the king.

"Blessed be you to the Lord, who have shewn this mercy to your master Saul, and have buried him. And now the Lord surely will render you mercy and truth, and I also will requite you for this good turn, because you have done this thing. Let your hands be strengthened, and be ye men of valour."

Among the cities of Juda, Hebron remembered the days of Abraham. The city overlooked the Valley of Mambre, made cool by fresh water and rich in grass. After he parted from Lot, Abraham led his flock there, and raised an altar to God in thanksgiving. At Hebron his wife Sara died and was buried in a cave in the valley. And Abraham purchased a field around that cave — the first property owned by the Hebrews in the land of Canaan.

In that famous city David was proclaimed King of Juda. King of Juda only, not King of Israel. Not all the royal family had fallen on the mountains of Gelboe. Saul had one son left, Isboseth, and he was protected and guided by Abner.

But Isboseth was not the man his father was. He was

not even of Jonathan's stature. His kingdom would never have risen from the ruins of Gelboe had not Abner led the son of Saul by the hand. "Abner, general of Saul's army," says the Book of Kings, "took Isboseth the son of Saul and led him about through the camp, and made him king over Galaad, and over Gessuri, and over Jezrahel, and over Benjamin and over all Israel."

The soldiers loved and feared Abner. They hailed the son of Saul, because he was accompanied by their *sarsaba,* their general.

At Hebron, on the other hand, David, champion of the tribe of Juda, David the young lion, youthfully sure of himself, climbed up toward the city of Abraham. Long and harsh though the years of exile and persecution had been, he seemed to be neither worn by privation nor heavy with weariness. In the desert the constant thought of God had supported and reinvigorated him:

O God, my God, to thee do I watch at break of day
For thee my soul hath thirsted;
For thee, my flesh, O how many ways!
In a desert land, and where there is no way, and no water.

Onward he marched toward Hebron with the lightness and grace of the victor of Goliath. Unarmed, his red hair bound with a linen scarf, with his harp at his side and sandals on his feet, David appeared before the Jews as the anointed of Samuel. Behind him, glaring and anxious, the sons of Sarvia struggled for place among curious onlookers and ambitious courtiers. Their arms shone like their faces and clattered as they brushed against each other, looked at each other and laughed.

Joab, Abisai, and Asael were gloriously happy. In following David these youths had risked death, but neither danger nor exhaustion nor difficulties had dampened their ardor. In their wild impatience the sons of Sarvia had more than once toyed with thoughts of betrayal and reprisals. But ever since David had turned them from the paths of iniquity, they had remained obedient and loyal to their uncle's will. Now the path David strode so confidently led upward toward the city of Hebron, and in pleased surprise they followed their leader with the eagerness of children.

After David, the sons of Sarvia would inherit the highest posts in the new kingdom. Joab in particular nourished in his heart — though he did not show it on his face — the hope of becoming the *sarsaba* of the Jewish army. In those days every man in the tribe of Juda who bore a shield and a spear placed himself under David's command, clear evidence of the strength the lion of Juda had attained.

Joab was delighted: up till then he had been in command of only a handful of men enthusiastic but restless. He already saw himself at the head of a redoubtable and well-organized army, finally meeting Abner's pursuing army in the field. In all the tribe of Juda there was no warrior so strong and enduring as Joab. Even his brothers, no less courageous than he, had to concede his prodigious tenacity in wearing the enemy down.

After the proclamation David went off at once to war, leaving Isboseth to worry about their rival claims. David felt safe at Hebron, whereas Isboseth, the last prince of a defeated dynasty, realized that only in successful battle could he restore the honor of the prostrate throne.

Meanwhile, realizing that Abner would attack, David put Joab in command of his army. By this move the son of Sarvia could prove his worth in the coming battle and

David would not stain his hands with Israelite blood.

Joab was a rough man and an impatient one and he saw nothing strange in men of the tribe of Benjamin and of the tribe of Juda fighting against one another. Eager to measure his strength against Abner's, he would have been the first to attack if David had not ordered him to wait till the enemy made the first move.

After Saul's death, however, Abner lost confidence. Only his honor as a soldier prevented him from giving up the fight. His oath of allegiance to Saul bound him to the last and weak descendant of the royal household. When he saw the army of Juda near the pool of Gabaon, bearing aloft the standards of the first tribe of Israel, his heart failed him. The sons of the same father were fighting against one another: the unity of Israel was shattered.

Joab did not think of this. For him Abner's warriors were merely the enemy against whom he must wrench in battle the title of *sarsaba*. Then Abner came to Joab and his face was sad and grief-stricken.

"To save bloodshed," he said, "let the young men rise and fight in our presence. Whoever wins, to him shall be the victory."

Joab hesitated. Then, unwillingly, perhaps thinking of David, he agreed.

So the champions of Juda and the champions of Benjamin came forward, each twelve strong. And every one, catching his fellow by the head, thrust his sword into the side of his adversary, and they fell down together in the same spot where they met.

Joab's eyes flashed fiercely. When the victory seemed in doubt, he rushed violently into their midst and started a general fight.

The battle lasted the whole day. Though Abner and

Joab fought with equal valor, old Abner was the more prudent and sagacious, Joab more hotheaded and fierce. Throughout the day the outcome of the battle hung in the balance. Toward evening Abner gave the signal to withdraw. At that the three sons of Sarvia went mad with rage. Thirsting for his blood, they hurled themselves against Abner.

Asael, the wild roe, pursued Saul's old captain with the swiftness of light. Sarvia's youngest son seemed to be intoxicated with his own speed. Covered by his shield and dragging his spear, he began to run faster and faster. Abner recognized him. He could easily have killed him, but he took pity on his intrepid youth. When he ran, Asael looked even more beautiful than he was. His pink, quivering nostrils drank in the air. His hair streamed behind his head which he flung back exposing his throat and the jugular vein swollen with blood.

As he ran Abner noticed the young man's vulnerable points, but he took no pleasure in it now. On the contrary, he felt only regret and bitterness. Every now and then, in the heat of the pursuit, he shouted to him: "Enough, Asael, go back. Do not follow me so tenaciously lest I be obliged to stab thee to the ground."

Asael did not hear him or else those words of moderation only served to augment his fury. To him they were words of surrender, not pity. He bit his lower lip, dried by the heat of the pursuit, and bared his teeth in a smile as he redoubled his efforts.

"Enough, Asael, go back." Breathing hard, Abner repeated his plea for the last time. He was an able warrior. Scarcely a second he paused as with a backward thrust of his spear he struck Asael in the groin, piercing him through, and Asael died on the spot.

His brothers came up. They did not even look at the body. So great was their fury that not even revenge could have whipped them into a more towering rage. But neither Joab nor Abisai was so swift as that brother who now lay stretched on the ground. Abner was able to gain a little advantage. At the top of the hill he halted. In their mad pursuit the two brothers exposed the back of their necks between helmet and cuirass, but Abner did not want to kill them.

"Stop!" he cried to them in piteous accents. "Stop! Knowest thou not it is dangerous to drive people to despair? Shalt thy sword rage unto utter destruction?"

The *sarsaba's* voice rang with such firm determination to fight, mingled with the sharp grief of one who has lost all hope, that the two brothers gave up the chase.

As the sun set, the dying day cast a sad and ashen light over the dead and wounded on the battlefield. There was a brief respite while night fell and divided the two armies. All night long Abner marched his men to put as much distance as possible between them and Gabaon. Joab and Abisai, also marching all night, reached Hebron just at twilight, carrying in their arms the body of their dead brother.

Like all weak men, Isboseth showed no gratitude toward Abner. Because of a woman he reproached and humiliated the old *sarsaba.* Abner was exceedingly wroth. "Am I a dog's head against Juda this day," he said with the fury of the disillusioned, "who have shewn mercy to the house of Saul thy father . . . and have not delivered thee into the hands of David? And hast thou sought this day against me to charge me with a matter concerning a woman?"

Isboseth feared Abner, but he did not love him. Humiliated by his reprimand, he turned ungrateful. He had inherited his father's suspicious nature, his unstable emotions and flightiness.

Abner declared he would abandon him: "So do God to Abner and more also, unless as the Lord hath sworn to David, so do I to him, that the kingdom be translated from the house of Saul."

He sent messengers to David and David joyfully received his antagonist's submission. But before he permitted Abner to come to Hebron he imposed one condition only: that Abner bring with him Michol, Saul's daughter, David's devoted wife.

Since David had fled from the kingdom of Gabaa, Michol had not rejoined her banished husband. She had remained in her empty apartments among the last of the idols, to weep, forgotten and almost a prisoner in the royal palace, exposed to Merob's cold, disdainful smile, her father's suspicion and Jonathan's pitying glances. She was estranged from her family, separated from her husband and from her father. David could not return till after that father's death, and because Michol longed for David's arrival, she dared not raise her eyes to her father lest Saul read his doom in them. Sensing the impending ruin of his house, Jonathan was more resigned in his despair. On the other hand, Michol was like one with one foot over the threshold, who hears the rumble of ruin, weeps for those inside with whom she would like to die but runs toward those waiting for her on the outside.

To make another life for her, Saul, who considered David an outlaw, gave her in marriage to Phaltiel, son of Lais, and Michol now knew the pain of a second separation. She could not forget David; but Phaltiel, a kind man and in love with her, was a good husband. She had no children, and Phaltiel was like a boy bewitched by her. Nor could she resist the pleasure she took in his mute and faithful devotion. David had always been absent-minded, absorbed in matters Michol could neither see nor gauge. She had often surprised a serious, thoughtful expression on her husband's face, but David evaded her questions with a flick of his eyelashes, the way she used to brush off a hesitant dove from the window sill with her hand.

Phaltiel, instead, was neither secretive nor mysterious. Those lovesick eyes of his held no shadows in their depths when they gazed at her. She could see herself mirrored in them, smiling, gratified by so much loyalty and adoration.

Away from Michol, David often thought of her, recalling their past life together. In combat, in dangerous flights, in the desert, in the dark of the caves, the thought of Michol came to him like the thought of peace. David smiled at it as at an illusion and drove it away as a trick of the imagination. He had known other women in his life — women with the determined face and ways of Abigail, capable of any emprise, any political maneuver.

But when he was crowned in Hebron, his thoughts sped at once to Michol as lightly as innocent desire. Who better than she could enjoy his triumph? At last she would be able to share in that mystery which, in the royal palace of Gabaa, she could not penetrate without horror.

Therefore David sent word to Abner that he would not receive him unless he was accompanied by Michol's smiling and enchanting face. Saul's passionate daughter, the girl with the warm heart, received the news with joy. David wanted her back. David still loved her. She was no longer just the princess, the much-desired prize. To be the daughter of Saul was no longer a privilege, but a disgrace. If David made his recovery of her a condition of peace, that meant that he loved her and that "his soul had remained steadfast to her soul."

But this time her joy at being recalled was marred by the thought of Phaltiel. Silent, his eyes filled with dismay, Phaltiel looked questioningly at Michol: the woman's cry of joy became a moan. As a mother, suffering, yet seeks to console her child, so Michol tried to comfort Phaltiel. But Phaltiel did not even listen to her: he wept, wept in silence, with no word of lament or reproach.

Michol's happiness lasted only a second — a second of forgetfulness. Then began the torture of preparations. Phaltiel followed her from room to room as she selected her gowns; he followed her into her bedroom where she made herself beautiful, and tears ran silently down his pale cheeks. Phaltiel's very presence was painful to her but she did not have the courage to send him away. Each act of hers performed before him seemed more than cruel, even shameless, her choice of objects an offense to Phaltiel's suffering, her languid motions, as she dressed, a hideous wound to his jealousy. Her too-fervent heart, her heart made for love and doomed to suffer, lay heavy in her breast. In the light of her desires it seemed to her black and bruised from beating and from being beaten too hard.

Even when Abner escorted her to Hebron, Phaltiel did not stir from her side. Swathed in veils, Michol rode a magnificently caparisoned ass and Phaltiel followed her afoot, weeping continuously.

All of Michol's longing drew her to David, but pity and affection made her turn to Phaltiel. She would have leapt from her mount and run to dry those tears with her veil but, as she could not, she, too, wept.

When they came within sight of Hebron, Abner refused to let Phaltiel go any farther. Setting his mule across the unhappy man's path, he forced him to leave them. Phaltiel did not have the strength to turn his back on the cortege. He stood there, motionless. Tears gushed even more violently from his swollen eyelids as, through eyes smarting from every ray of light, he watched Michol's veiled figure disappear up the hill toward the city of the new king.

Joab was not present when Abner and Michol arrived. David had kept this news from him and to get him away from Hebron, he had sent him out in pursuit of marauders. Now, rich in booty taken from the raiders, and well pleased with himself, Joab returned. He had sent a caravan of camels laden with merchandise ahead; behind him, in among the soldiers, came the prisoners and slaves; and bringing up the rear trotted a herd of asses laden with leather bags and pouches. Flushed with the wine he had drunk, his stomach replete with succulent food, Joab laughed and joked in high good spirits. At long last, here in Hebron, David had recognized his ability in war and in peace.

When Joab was told that Abner had been David's guest for several days, and that, as a pledge of peace, he had brought Michol, still as passionate as a turtledove, the light went out of his eyes and the blood rushed to his head.

His dream was threatened. Abner, reconciled with David, would retain his title of *sarsaba*. All Joab's efforts would have been in vain: his courage, flouted; his fame, forgotten. He would be obliged to yield to his enemy the highest honor a soldier could attain.

The mere possibility was unbearable. Joab did not discuss it even with David; he did not complain to anyone.

The lineaments of his face barely stiffened. He smiled to himself, wrinkled his ferocious face, and, without a qualm, promptly made his decision.

Unknown to David, he sent a messenger to overtake Abner on his way back to the tribe of Benjamin and inform him that the king desired him to return to Hebron. Wearing a friendly smile on his face, Joab met Abner outside of the city and, under pretext of speaking to him privately, he led him aside and stabbed him in the groin.

When David heard this, he rent his clothes, covered his head with ashes, took up his harp, and for Abner improvised the mournful *quinah:*

> Not as cowards are wont to die,
> Hath Abner died.
> Thy hands were not bound,
> Nor thy feet laden with fetters;
> But as men fall before the children of iniquity
> Did'st thou fall.

But, David did not punish the "children of iniquity," because they were the sons of Sarvia.

The day Abner died, David felt for the first time the full weight of his past. Up till then he had depended too much on Joab, on Abisai, on Asael, on all the children of iniquity, for him to judge impartially.

He did not like Joab. The latter was too cruel, too harsh even for David. More than once, on meeting Joab's eye, David had felt some force resisting him: either the ice of disdain or the tenacity of the other man's will.

On the other hand, he could not forget those days in the cave of Odollam. At that time he had been an outlaw. Any man could have raised his hand against him. To satisfy his hunger he had been forced to beg bread; to arm himself he had cheated a priest; to shelter from the rain he had hidden in a cave like a wild beast. And in that cave he could have died, deserted by all, had not Sarvia come to him, driving before her those three youths, bewitched by his exploits. With his seven brothers the cave had seemed like a prison to David; with his nephews it had grown bright, had become a stronghold.

Then came the gray and yellow desert, the bare hills around the Salt Sea; the deep and treacherous woods; nights in the open sheepfold, days of marching; hunger, thirst, privation, pursuit, battles, treachery, and death. The three youths, with Joab at their head, had never held back, never spared themselves. David had always been compelled to restrain them, never to spur them on.

Now he saw how hard it was to incline to goodness men in the habit of yielding to their chaotic passions. He himself could be mild or severe, merciful or cruel, rash or prudent, reckless or wise, choosing whichever seemed to him the better and more expedient means.

But with a man like Joab, in whom instinct outweighed judgment, those wild outbursts were inherent and inevitable. Joab had opened Abner's veins at the gates of Hebron as he would have slit Saul's throat in the cave of Engaddi and Nabal's stomach on the threshing floors of Maon.

David did not have the stamina to punish Joab for killing Abner. He left the decision in God's hands:

"May it [the blood of Abner] come upon the head of Joab and upon all his father's house; and let there not fail from the house of Joab one . . . that is a leper, or that holdeth the distaff, or that falleth by the sword or that wanteth bread."

Not that the arm of justice was shortened. This was

demonstrated shortly afterward when two other scoundrels, who attempted to gain favor through treachery, were put to death. They belonged to the tribe of Benjamin. Foreseeing that, with Abner dead, Isboseth would soon reign on the throne, they planned to prevent this by another regicide and to be the ones to offer David the crown of Israel.

One oppressively hot summer's day, in the early morning hours, two brothers chanced to be in the neighborhood of the royal palace of Gabaa. The sun, reflected against the white walls and the clouds of dust, was blinding. No one paid any attention to the passers-by, who staggered as if overcome by the burning heat.

Even the royal guards lounged back in shady corners or under the dusty and almost colorless trees. The gate, red-hot, was deserted. Baana and Recab passed through unnoticed.

Within the palace, silence and darkness. Their pupils, contracted by the glare, opened with difficulty in that gloom which, as it lessened, gradually revealed the deserted corridors and empty rooms. All the courtiers had retired to their own apartments. In front of the king's bedroom a woman crouched on the floor. Busy sifting corn, she had fallen asleep over her task. What had become of Saul's former grandeur? Where was the power of his royal family? There, leaning against the wall as if forgotten, stood the king's spear. Isboseth slept, but no one watched over the sleep of Saul's youngest son.

Recab and Baana raised the curtain to the royal bedchamber and no one stayed their hand. That silent, somnolent palace, where neither sentries nor loyal followers watched over the life of their king, was a symbol of the reign that was slipping to a close in inertia and apathy.

Though he was forty years old, Isboseth was as weak as

a babe. Not a soldier, but a woman, guarded the threshold of his bedchamber like a nurse and, indifferent to the welfare of that orphaned king, she, too, slept.

Unmoved by any feeling of pity, Recab and Baana passed by the woman. Isboseth's quiet slumber failed to arouse their compassion. They cut off his head and stole cautiously from the palace before anyone knew what had happened.

All afternoon they walked in the burning sunshine, carrying Isboseth's head wrapped in a cloth. And they went on walking all night in the moonlight. By morning they arrived in Hebron to show David the head shriveled by the sun and rotted with dew.

David drew back in horror. Struck down in sleep, and shrunken now in death, Isboseth's face looked startlingly like the pale, delicate face of Michol.

DAVID, KING OF ISRAEL

BEFORE he died Abner said to the ancients of the tribe: "Both yesterday and the day before you sought for David that he might reign over you. Now then do it; because the Lord hath spoken to David, saying: By the hand of my servant David I will save my people Israel from the hands of the Philistines and of all their enemies."

The ancients waited, though not for long. In all their motions the ancients were cautious and deliberate. But when Isboseth, too, was slain, they realized that David was destined to be king. With Saul dead, Jonathan dead, Isboseth dead, and finally even Abner, that tangle of doubts, suspicions, and passions had been resolved in the most obvious and tragic way. David only, alone and serene, mourning but not remorseful, wielding the authority of power but not of tyranny, was without equal in Israel.

Then the ancients set out to join him in Hebron, saying: "Behold we are thy bone and thy flesh. Thou shalt feed the people of God and thou shalt be prince over Israel."

David overcame opposition, resolved doubts. When the ancients stood before him, their speech was forceful and unusual: "We are thy bone and thy flesh." Never had that phrase been used before save between husband and wife in the Book of Genesis. "Thou shalt feed my people." Till now that prerogative had belonged only to the Lord.

But David did not forget his Creator and the might of "Him who is." The true shepherd of all men was, and always would be, the Lord. The Promised Land was not the land over which David now ruled in undisputed sway, but the land toward which a man yearns even in a city, even between four walls or two rivers. Toward that fatherland God leads souls as the shepherd leads his flocks; God who, in David's poetic language, was always coolness and shade, never sun and high noon.

The shepherd fears the sun that destroys his pasture lands and dries up springs. God does not fear the sun, because His tent is firmly anchored in eternity, and neither frost nor fire can lay waste His pastures. And in the sun where our pastures would be scorched, where our souls would die of thirst, God, the Supreme Shepherd, "has pitched His tent forever."

David was thirty years old when he was crowned king of Israel. Eighteen years had passed since Samuel anointed him, and for seven years and six months he reigned in Hebron over Juda. Not once did he make a mistake through overhastiness, nor commit an injustice through overgreediness. In his day of triumph he could sing with a frankness almost bordering on arrogance:

The Lord will reward me according to my justice:
And according to the cleanness of my hands he will render to me.

Because I have kept the ways of the Lord,
And have not wickedly departed from my God.
For all His judgments are in my sight; and his precepts I have not removed from me.
And I shall be perfect with him:
And shall keep myself from my iniquity.
And the Lord will recompense me according to my justice:
And according to the cleanness of my hands in the sight of His eyes.

And behold, after the ancients there came to Hebron six thousand eight hundred men from Juda, armed with shields and spears, well appointed to fight. Seven thousand one hundred came from the tribe of Simeon. Four thousand six hundred from the tribe of Levi.

The tribe of Benjamin, still looking askance at the man from Juda who had been set upon Saul's throne, sent only three thousand slingers. From the tribe of Ephraim, on the other hand, came twenty thousand eight hundred men, all strong and of good extraction, while the twin tribe of Manasse sent eighteen thousand.

The men of Isaacar, learned in forecasting the weather and in knowledge of the seasons, arrived two hundred strong, having at their command as many men under them. Then came the men from Zabulon, fifty thousand strong — simple-hearted men and as numerous as grasshoppers. From the tribe of Nephtali a thousand princes, with thirty-seven thousand men. From Dan, twenty-eight thousand men. From Aser, forty thousand. Last of all, one hundred and twenty thousand armed men from the tribes of Ruben and of Gad on the other side of the Jordan. And, one and all, they went up to Hebron to acclaim David King of Israel.

All those warriors from all those tribes had to be formed into a military organization. Saul had founded his reign on the military might of Benjamin. David, instead, wanted all the tribes to participate in war each with their own men, incorporated in an army that would be as unified as a nation.

To that end he divided the mass of armed men into groups of thousands which in turn were subdivided into groups of a hundred each. Each hundred was commanded by an officer and each thousand by a general and all under the supreme command of the *sarsaba* and of the king.

However, David did not include in that arrangement the old comrades of his exile, but formed them into three companies, known as the *gibborim,* or heroes. They were the veterans of Odollam, of Ceila, of Siceleg, of Zif, and of Engaddi; men who had followed him faithfully, and, sometimes, grudgingly; those who had escaped pursuit and ambush. Under David's command they had champed at the bit and restrained their blows. Under Joab's they had killed and tortured. Hardened by the desert, worn by privations, scarred by wounds, they had spent their youth in hide-outs and caves, out of loyalty to their young leader. David knew them man for man. He had only to look at them with his beautiful eyes and they swelled with pride. Between David and his men there was a deep, silent bond: their mutual memories of the hard life and the sufferings they had endured together. One place, one action, one name — and suddenly all of them remembered events long past and shared in common, memories at which they trembled with emotion.

David could never forget those comrades. Even their faults, even the grief they had caused him, were dear and precious to him.

> If I have done harm to him who has done good to me
> May I fall before my enemies.

Those rough men, often deaf to his commands and always restless, had been good for him. Their life in common, the dangers and privations shared and endured together, their readiness to help one another, had shown the lonely shepherd, the harpist-courtier a new side of human endurance. Even the efforts spent in controlling those men "quick to shed blood," in guiding comrades who "did not know the paths of peace," had not been wasted. David felt all the firmer and more secure in his ability to govern men. Nothing that had happened in those eighteen years of preparation for his reign had been in vain.

He arranged for the six hundred *gibborim* to remain under the command of Sarvia's second son, the one who had followed him into Saul's camp and was satisfied with the cup of water that stood at Saul's head in lieu of a cup of blood. Joab, instead, because of his recent crime, received neither honors nor rewards.

The Israelites did not have a capital. Each tribe boasted its own cities seized or captured in battle from the people of Canaan, but none of those cities had risen in fame and power above the others. Gabaa, the stronghold of Benjamin, the royal city of Saul; Masfa, where the ancients gathered in the days of the Judges; Bethlehem, city of

David's birth; Silo, the seat of the Ark; Hebron, Abraham's city and David's capital. Each one of those cities had some special distinction or merit, but none could impose its authority over the others.

David, King of Israel, intended to establish his throne in a city without peer. A return to Gabaa, Saul's gloomy palace, might look like an ugly display of victory. To choose Bethlehem as the capital city and to build the royal palace on Booz's granaries would be to exalt his own family over all the tribes. If he stayed in Hebron, he would be favoring Juda and scorning Benjamin. To go to Silo meant giving greater importance to the throne than to the Ark, placing royal authority above that of the high priests.

The choice of a capital was not easy for a man anxious not to show partiality between the tribes or to cause any rivalry. In the center of Palestine, dividing the tribes of the north from the tribes of the south, and dominating the great valley of Jehoshaphat, stood a rocky promontory to which no one attached any importance other than as a lookout. Though they had built a small fortress on the very top, the Jebusites had stuck no more than a thorn in the heart of Israel.

Neither the Judges nor Saul had ever succeeded in removing that eagle's nest from between the sister tribes. The road up to the Jebusite stronghold was apparently hidden and impassable. The last crown of rock on which stood another crown of wall rendered the promontory invincible. In addition a waterfall, cascading down from the rock, made it possible for that already strong position to hold out indefinitely.

David raised his eyes to that almost-deserted rocky stronghold. No tribe could claim possession of it. The fortress had no history. The Israelites were satisfied to look at it from below and circle around it, sighing, whereas the Jebusites, secure in their position, paid almost no attention to its defense and were in the habit of saying that the post could easily be held by the lame and the blind.

Its central position in the middle of the tribes and of the country gave the Jebusite stronghold both military and political importance. The more David looked at that promontory rising from the dark background of the valley of Jehoshaphat, the more determined he was to build his new city on those rocks.

But when they heard of his plan, the Israelites were greatly alarmed. Perhaps the shepherd king did not realize the difficulties involved in driving out that band of mountain goats. The Jebusites laughed: "Thou shalt not come in hither," they sent word to him, "unless thou take away the blind and the lame."

Indeed, as David's strategists tried to point out to him, the storming of the Jebusite city would be particularly difficult for men like the Israelites, who had so little experience in direct attack upon fortified cities. For, with the exception of Jericho, whose walls had fallen miraculously, the Hebrews had conquered the Palestinian cities either by surprise, or by the treachery of the inhabitants.

David knew this, but his clear and limpid eyes continued to gaze up at the Jebusite stronghold, while a smile crept into the corners of his mouth, half-opened as he listened to voices his men could not hear. Perhaps the voices of the sons of Core came to him across some memory of the future:

With the joy of the whole earth
Is Mount Sion founded,
On the sides of the North,
The city of the great King.
In her houses God shall be known,
When he shall protect her.

Surround Sion, and encompass her:
Tell ye in her towers.
Set your heart on her strength;
And distribute her houses.

Creaking machines approached the slopes of Sion. The disdainful sneer on the Jebusites' lips vanished. Marching amid the dust of chariots and the din of implements of war came not a band of shepherds, but an army more to be feared than the Philistines. The shepherd-king, the harpist-king, David, sweet singer and enchanter, well knew that charm could capture hearts, but to conquer cities one must have catapults, battering rams, and moving fortresses.

His capture of Sion would be the affirmation of his power. He had no intention of being hurled back off the rocky promontory by the blind and the lame, so he ordered wide runways constructed and closed in to lay siege to the fortress. And yet he did not want to starve the Jebusites into surrendering. His *gibborim* were fighting under the eyes of all Israel. They must wring victory from the enemy in one violent attack, and on that victory found the royal house of David.

However, the citadel of Sion offered stubborn resistance. David's machines made a breach in the thick walls, but even through the ruins it would have been difficult to break into the stronghold. Then David promised the title of *sarsaba* to the first man to enter those walls.

Stripped of his command, alone and raging with fury,

Joab circled the rock, measuring all the possible passages, calculating distances, studying the terrain in every particular. At last he discovered a large passage that ran down like a huge water pipe from beneath the walls of the fortress. For days and nights he guarded the passage like a snarling cur. No one must go up there before he did. When the walls of the citadel began to open, he was the first to climb up, at first cautiously and silently, searching for sure footholds in the jutting stones, pulling himself up by sheer strength of his arms.

When the Jebusites saw that sweating, bloodshot face below the walls, they tried to throw him back. Joab made a daring effort. Drawing his sword, he exposed himself to attack. Stones and javelins were hurled at him. For a second he staggered on the glacis, then with a shout flung himself on the enemy. His roar was heard by the entire army.

Abisai, who was standing ready with his six hundred *gibborim,* gave a start. "Joab!" Stones rolled down on the feet and heads of the attackers; there was shouting and groaning. Reaching the walls, Abisai tried anxiously to catch sight of Joab. He was afraid of finding him wounded and in torture, but Joab was standing at the well with the defeated enemy in a circle around him, bathing the bruises and cuts made by his crawl along the rocky passageway.

To build the new city David needed workmen and Phoenician material, especially from Tyre. The Hebrews did not know how to put up walls, to build, to chisel and carve, to work metals, mold vases, or paint the walls of houses. The chosen people had always led a pastoral life. To follow his calling, Abraham had become a shepherd, and from that day the Hebrews had interpreted every significant event in their history in the light of sheep rearing.

And the history of the Hebrews had been one long pilgrimage. Not by plowing, not by planting save rarely, not by cutting roads or digging canals had the Israelites produced a nomad people. Their life had become one with their goal: their history nothing but a tangle of meandering roads between the sea, the valley of the Nile, and the valley of the Euphrates.

The tent in which they lived also sat lightly on the ground and could vanish in the twinkling of an eye. To pitch a tent was equivalent to asking for hospitality, to take down the tent meant departure. The Hebrews were always ready to be on the move. Their treasures did not rot in the soil. And after they had moved on there would be only a few straws left to show where their camp had been.

Without homesickness, without regret, without any earthly attachments, they moved from a place where they had lived a long time to a place where they would live even longer. This nomadic life had prevented the Hebrews from practicing the art of building. The Israelites did not know how to place stone upon stone artistically. When they sacrificed to God they rolled up a few stones, made a rude altar, and laid their offerings on it. When a faithful wife or an aged father died, the family bought a cave and sealed the entrance with a rounded rock like a millstone. All they could do was to roll stones as they rolled up their carpets before moving on or as they rolled flocks of wool into balls to take to market.

Moving thus from place to place, they left behind them nothing but consecrated stones or graves or wells. When the Canaanites wanted to wipe out Abraham's footprints from their land, they filled with sand the wells he had dug.

No other sign remained to testify to his passage: not a hovel, not a village, not a road, not a stronghold built by the Israelites.

David asked the Phoenician king of Tyre to send him workmen and artists. To them he entrusted the construction of the "city of David" on the top of the hill of Sion, and for the first time in their history the Hebrews, stunned and suspicious, watched the building of a city. They saw land surveyors map boundaries, set up base lines, draw square corners and center curves. And after them came the builders, with plumb lines, rulers, and calipers; stonecutters with chiselpoints, mallets, and awls; blacksmiths with anvils and forges. Glaziers and goldsmiths worked in the fire like demons; potters and brickmakers in water like fish. Filled with clamor and shouting, the Mount of Sion was a reincarnation of the Tower of Babel.

The Israelites were fascinated by the Phoenicians' skill, but they half-expected the confusion of tongues to repeat itself, with the potters carrying mud to the goldsmiths and the builders' helper carrying the cauldron full of chips to the men who needed lime for their walls.

Instead, just the opposite occurred on the Mount of Sion. Out of that confusion, that chaos and that shouting, came order and harmony. Walls began to rise on their foundations; stairs curved upward in graceful flights; carved doorjambs were set up at the sides of the doors, the architraves placed horizontal across the walls. One by one or grouped together, according to the design, columns were set up on bases carved by the chisel as delicately as if they were gold.

David himself watched the work admiringly. Even he was amazed at the Phoenicians' ability to join huge squared stones together by filling the wall with bags of earth and dentils. "Jerusalem, which is built as a city, which is compact together."

He was flattered by the number of the decorations and the costliness of the material. It might well be said that the city had "foundations of sapphires, bulwarks of jasper, and gates of graven stones, and all thy borders of desirable stones."

The Phoenician architects, architects of a rich merchant race, tended more to display than to refinement. More decorators than builders, they were lavish in their use of gold, precious stones, polished marble, and perfumed woods. The Hebrews, naïve and unsubtle, were easily deceived by the dazzling glitter and the perfection of the decorations.

Thus the city of Jerusalem was built. And it looked as if the palaces of Tyre had been transplanted to the heights of Sion.

This worried the old Israelites and made them suspicious. The city which, in the history of the Chosen People, was supposed to be the symbol of the eternal land; the city for which all men would sigh as the symbol of salvation and glory; the "room of plenty," the "pavilion that will not be removed," the city of the twelve foundations, the city of pure gold, with walls of jasper, which the angelic surveyors would measure at the end of time with the ruler of gold — had risen in their day in imitation of the cities of idolators.

As the old Iraelites passed the foot of the hill and looked up at the new buildings, they felt greater sorrow than when they had passed over the same road and seen the Jebusite sentinels on the enemy citadel. It seemed as if the young king had denied and defiled the whole history of the Chosen People. Where now were the old traditions, the ancient customs, even those outward signs that had always distinguished the Israelites from the worshipers of idols?

Accompanying himself on his harp, David sang praises to the one God, but even his song betrayed a new feeling. There was too much joy in it and the sad, serious Israelites, for whom God's predilection often meant sorrow and gloom, listened to the young poet-king with a feeling of sacrilegious pleasure and servile fear.

For David the Lord had ceased to mean sadness, or servitude, or fear: He was confident joy, freedom, gratitude, a great heart, courageous faith, and exultation:

> I will give praise to thee, O Lord, with my whole heart:
> I will relate all thy wonders.
> I will be glad and rejoice in thee:
> I will sing to thy name, O thou most high.

The hill of Sion resounded with noise from the yards of the builders; smooth walls and precise corner edges were set in, polished columns erected, precious metals beaten. It was all new, beautiful, and glittering. But newer than any recent work, more daring than any dangerous construction, freer and more marvelous was the song of the young king.

The land grew rich in monuments on the hill of Sion, but David's song wrought a greater miracle: he was able to brighten with joy, to make heaven with the wonderful works of God seem nearer and shining:

> The heavens shew forth the glory of God,
> And the firmament declareth the work of his hands.
> Day to day uttereth speech,
> And night to night sheweth knowledge.

There are no speeches nor languages,
Where their voices are not heard.
Their sound hath gone forth into all the earth:
And their words unto the ends of the world.

The patriarchs had made miraculous alliances and signed solemn pacts with the Lord. The judges, fighting in the name of the Lord, had never failed to keep His law. All the Hebrew people had remained faithful and subject to the Lord in fear of divine anger and vengeance. But no one had ever approached the Lord with David's frankness and trust, no one, as quick and free as he, had dared to gain the right hand of the Lord through love:

I will love thee, O Lord, my strength!

When the Philistines learned that the slayer of Goliath ruled over Israel, that he was reorganizing the army and building his capital on the hill of Sion, they were envious and they feared his might. With the coming of spring, they gathered together their army in secret and promptly invaded the region.

The Philistines' swift move caught David by surprise. Jerusalem was like a young flowering plant, without any rough bark; all white palaces but no strong walls: a city, not yet a fortress. David realized that the defense of Jerusalem presented grave difficulties. Driving straight for the new and unprotected city the Philistines were also trying to cut off the roads running from south to north and so isolate David from the southern tribes who were more faithful to him and had richer harvests.

David's love of his new city did not make him tarry on the heights of Jerusalem. He fled hastily from his bright palace, deserted the maiden city, and with his army retreated toward Judea, or rather toward his native city of Bethlehem.

Spring passed into summer, the crops began to ripen, and those sudden roseate flushes which turn the green to yellow spread over the fields. David knew that country well. He knew that the land produced barley and corn in sufficient quantity to feed both inhabitants and soldiers. However, he did not go up to the granary city nor did he shut himself up within its walls. He preferred to occupy the terrain around the cave of Odollam. Making his home in the cave, he fortified the surrounding land with dried walls, valleys, and ditches, transforming his ancient hiding place into a regular fortress.

Summer reached its zenith; not a breath of air stirred in the plain of Odollam, smothered under a blanket of heat. Even the yellow crops turned dusty and ashen. The rivers dried up and their scorching beds were overrun with lizards. The springs moaned as if it hurt them to emerge from the cool rock into the parched heat of the air; their clear flow became a trickle, then nothing but a tired weeping, and at last even the few rare drops ceased to refresh the tufts of eel grass. The whole countryside was scorched, parched, and feverish.

David sat at the entrance to the cave as if stunned by the dazzling light. His comrades had flung themselves down in the shade hoping to find in sleep a little relief and coolness. Their breath issued from their parched throats in a sharp hiss.

As the king looked through that burning haze at the dusty outlines of his city he had only one desire. He remembered beside the gate of Bethlehem a fountain of the freshest water. As a boy he had drunk of it, cupping it in both hands, spilling it over his chin, his throat, and the shirt, open on his chest. He remembered how he had played with that cool water, squirting it at his companions or, laughing, had raised his streaming face from the stone basin.

The memory sharpened his thirst; it seemed almost impossible that there had ever been such easy treasure in the world. He could not get that fountain out of his thoughts; he kept seeing it clearer and more abundant than it really was; he could feel its delicious coolness on the thick, dusty taste in his mouth.

"Oh, that some man would give me water from the cistern of Bethlehem which is in the gate."

He spoke partly to himself, partly the better to taste, with the words, the deliciousness of that coveted water, but someone heard him. There was a light rustle in the brushwood growing at the opening of the cave, as if a green lizard had scampered through the hedge. Then silence. A few moments later the rustling was repeated but this time louder. David heard a sound like heavy breathing as though tired men were climbing the hill. With an effort he shook off his drowsiness. He did not realize that he had spoken, and it seemed to him that only a second had passed between his wish and his waking.

Three young men, sweating and half-dead from the heat, came and prostrated themselves at his feet, while the water jug they were carrying struck the ground and a stream of water gushed forth. Crossing the valley under that burning sun, the young men had gone to the gate of Bethlehem and, under attack from the Philistines who occupied the city, had drawn the water their king longed for.

David raised the jug. The water wet his hands, ran down his elbow, made him shiver. The three young men waited for him to put it to his lips. With mouths agape they followed the king's every motion. Their Adam's apples rose and fell under their sweating skin as if they were already swallowing with David the first draughts of that cool water.

But, after a moment's suspense, David said: "God forbid that I should do this in the sight of my God and should drink the blood of these men." And he poured the water from the jug onto the ground.

At the sound of the shower all the comrades leapt to their feet. Their eyes widened and their mouths were bitter, and moaning they stared at David as if they thought the heat had robbed him of his senses. The greedy earth sucked in the water till there was not even a dark spot left at the king's feet.

Then each man went back to his shadow. But the thirst of all was lessened as if the water with which David had made oblation to the earth had refreshed every man of them.

David waited, observing the movements of the Philistines, watching for the opportune moment when the enemy would be tired and distracted. Then he attacked, cut the enemy in half as the waters of a river are divided, and threw him back toward Gabaon.

The season was now well advanced; the crops harvested. The time for war was over, and when the Philistines withdrew, David returned to Jerusalem.

But if the battles were over for that year, the war itself could not be said to be at an end. The following year, in the spring, the Philistines equipped a much larger army and appeared on the plateau of Raphaim which looks westward toward Jerusalem.

This time David gathered around him thirty thousand young warriors and waited for the invasion. Trained by experience, the Philistines reinforced themselves in a pyramidal quadrilateral, protected on the left by impassable rocks and on the right by woods difficult to penetrate.

David consulted the Lord. "Go not up against them," was the reply, "but fetch a compass behind them, and when thou shalt hear the sound of one going in the tops of the pear trees, then shalt thou join battle: for then will the Lord go out before thy face to strike the army of the Philistines."

Those words clearly indicated an encircling movement which David carried out with great strategic skill. On the day of battle he brought up his army face to face with the army of the Philistines. The battle plan was for a frontal attack. Slingers and archers advanced and made the first breach in the enemy ranks. Then men armed with spears rushed in; finally both armies clashed in hand-to-hand fighting. After that the battle resolved into a series of duels or centered around a few knots of resistance.

Though the battle of Raphaim began with a frontal attack, David with three thousand picked warriors was not among the attacking force led by Joab. While Joab stormed the fortified quadrilateral, David turned the Philistines' flank and, protected by the woods, marched toward the west.

He waited deep in the woods till late afternoon. Then, just as the sun was sinking, there was a rustling in the treetops. A light breeze stirred the topmost branches, making a sound like rapid footsteps. David recognized that wind as the sign the Lord had indicated. And moving his *gibborim* out of the woods, he led them up to the plateau of Raphaim. The Philistines had held out all day against Joab's attacks and they were feeling confident of victory when the shouts of David and Abisai resounded to their rear. To escape the attack they fell back toward the rocks to the east of their camp and, dividing, scattered and fled wildly up the mountain paths, pursued and cut down by Abisai's *gibborim.*

David's two victories marked the end of the Philistines' military hegemony. They do not appear again as a threat in the history of the Israelites. Goliath had been in truth the symbol of their strength and their defeat.

On his way back to Jerusalem, David took with him as war booty the idols which the Philistines had carried to war and set up in the midst of their camp. He remembered the time when the Philistines had seized the Ark, which the Levites carried into battle in the days before Samuel was judge over the chosen people.

The Philistines' defeat at Raphaim may be said to have avenged the insult to the Ark. The idols of Dagon and Astarotte that fell into David's hands were burned as instruments of superstition. But while he was destroying the Philistine idols, he remembered the Ark and the neglect into which it had fallen. In David's plan, Jerusalem, the political capital of Israel, was to receive the Ark and become the holy city of the Israelite nation.

Lightly but solidly built on a frame of setim wood (perhaps acacia), two cubits and a half long and a cubit and a half wide, with a covering of gold within and without, suitably light in weight, the Ark was obviously intended for quick and easy transportation. To carry it, two bars of wood overlaid with gold were passed through four iron rings attached to the sides of the Ark. Though the bars were loose they were never to be removed from the rings: a clear sign that the Ark must always be ready to move on. Four Levites, two at one bar, two at the other, in short tunics and high boots, were to be ready at any moment and for any reason to lift the Ark and carry it easily. "Now in the Ark," says the Bible, "there was nothing else but the two tables of stone, which Moses put there at Horeb."

All the other objects of worship: candelabra, lamps, vases, were also made to be easily moved. The most cumbersome parts, like the table and the sacrificial altar, also had four rings through which bars were inserted.

And just as the Ark retained the signs and characteristics of Israelite nomadism, so the parts of the tabernacle that protected the Ark were constructed with an eye to lightness and mobility. Nothing that had to do with the Ark was fixed. Goats' skins, lined with woven byssus, hyacinth and violet and saffron in color and dyed twice, were held together by interlaced strings. The columns that supported the curtains reached to the ground, but rested on plinths of silver, so that while the Hebrews' tent was light, the tabernacle of their God did not weigh any more and was easily borne from one end of the land to the other.

David did not intend to keep the Ark a prisoner in Jerusalem, but to make it the highest glory of the nation. The Ark of the Covenant with God must not be sheltered in the house of a private individual, to become an object of fear rather than of love. But first of all David planned to reorganize and improve the forms of worship and the sacred liturgy which would be centered around the Ark. Gathering together all the descendants of Levi, he divided them into various orders. To the one he entrusted the administration of holy matters; to another the task of instruction; to still another that of worship. He encouraged and developed sacred music and the singing of chants. He himself composed hymns and psalms for popular festivals; he himself sang and taught singing before the Ark, to the glory of God.

And yet merely to carry the Ark to Jerusalem would not have been enough for him. He dreamed of constructing a temple more magnificent than his royal palace. "I dwell in a house of cedar, and the Ark of God is lodged in a house of skins." But the prophet Nathan forbade David to build the temple, for he was not worthy. Only his successor would be allowed to complete that task.

David obeyed the prophet, but he could not get that plan out of his mind. All his life long he had conceived plans and devised marvelous works. From the windows of his royal palace he could already see walls and ceilings and roofs shutting out the air from around the goatskin tent in which the Ark was preserved. He could see columns and beams of cedar set in place; pavements laid; walls rise.

Nor was he satisfied to dream. With the help of Phoenician architects, he himself, bending over his worktable, drew up the plans of the temple, the vestibule, the high priests' house, and the treasure, down to the smallest details. He sketched divisions and sections, mouldings and decorations, altars and basins. In addition he decided upon the shape, weight, and price of all the sacred utensils. He designed candelabra, censers, basins, and chalices. To Solomon, his son and heir, he left, along with the necessary gold and silver, a project "written by the hand of God Himself."

Therefore the temple which was later known as Solomon's was also the work of David, who provided the plans and the means to build it. But the harpist-king, the psalmist-king was permitted to show his devotion and his ardor only in song and dance.

The day when the Ark, drawn by white oxen, was

brought up to Jerusalem, David, drunk with joy, danced before all the people of Israel. He laid aside the garment of white, the insignia of the king, and, barefooted and with curls rumpled, he looked like a boy again. His eyes sparkled; blood rushed to his cheeks, which once more wore the rosy bloom of youth. He carried only his harp, from which he drew the sweetest notes as he sang:

> Lift up your gates, O ye princes,
> And be ye lifted up, O eternal gates:
> And the King of Glory shall enter in.
>   Who is this King of Glory?
> The Lord who is strong and mighty:
> The Lord mighty in battle.
> Lift up your gates, O ye princes,
> And be ye lifted up, O eternal gates:
> And the King of Glory shall enter in.
>   Who is this King of Glory?
> The Lord of hosts, he is the King of Glory.

David sang and danced in the midst of the people. Around him the women, those women who had once roused Saul's suspicions, accompanied the king's singing and dancing with timbrels and sistri. Filled with holy ardor, the *nabi* — the prophets — exulted and cried out with joy. Dust got in their throats and, added to their excitement, made them shout all the louder. The sun was blinding. The clanging of bells on the oxens' collars and the boom of the big feast bells vibrated in the hot, sultry air, making a deafening uproar.

Only Michol, alone and far away in thought, "watched from a window." She could not bring herself to rejoice with the others. David was like a drop of blood in the veins of his people. He seemed to have grown neither older nor prouder. The ashes of old age had not yet extinguished the flame of his hair; his body was still agile and his voice youthful.

Michol, instead, the daughter of Saul, the passionate girl, stood at the window as if turned to stone, her lips drawn, unsmiling, and her eyes veiled in sorrow. Perhaps she was thinking of the years when she, too, had danced and sung delightfully. Perhaps she was seeing in her mind's eye that day, long past, when the boy David returned to the palace. That day she had not been a stranger holding aloof from the exulting crowds. The women had sung then, too, and she had sung with them, sung and danced before that laughing youth who came toward her between lines of soldiers, with Goliath's armor on his back.

The presence of her father, of Merob and of Jonathan, had not intimidated her; on the contrary, she had become all the bolder. To be the daughter of the king, a princess of the blood royal, seemed to her an intolerable burden: she would have preferred to be merely a woman, free to yield to her desire, to throw herself into the general rejoicing, smiling at everyone because everyone smiled at David.

Now, instead, her memories weighed heavily on her. For the first time Michol felt that she belonged to her dead. Saul, Jonathan, Abinadab, Melchisua, all fallen on the Mount of Gelboe; Isboseth, the last of her brothers, betrayed and decapitated; Merob far away, her name almost forgotten in Israel. She, Michol, was only the orphan, the sister of princes dethroned and rendered powerless by death.

Even Phaltiel, who loved her, was now among the shades. Michol felt completely alone. No one fought David for her anymore, David who danced and sang in praise of his God.

And the God he exalted had liberated him from his

enemies: confounding the informers, making the traitors fall into the trap they themselves had dug, smoothing his path for him, causing the crowns of his rivals to fall before him — and with the crowns, their heads!

Michol shuddered. Her flashing eyes became as cold as ice, her smile as sharp as a blade. Her inheritance from Saul spread through her blood, caused her to feel on her temples the cold band of lucid and despairing thoughts.

That evening when he returned to the palace David found her still with that taut smile on her lips and that icy band around her temples. He was tired, for the banquet, where he had presented every citizen of Jerusalem with a cake of bread, a portion of roasted ox meat, and a wheat pie fried in oil, had lasted a long time. After the banquet had come the languor and prostration usual at the end of festivities and David, dismayed to find his joy suddenly transformed into melancholy, was seeking the peace and silence of his rooms.

He smiled, but in his extreme fatigue the effort was painful to him. Michol thought he was smiling in complacent vanity. All day long she had not spoken a word. Now, silent and hostile, she looked at her husband, watching his every motion. He was so sure of himself, so much the master of himself, the ruler. Michol was almost jealous of that confident air which made her feel even more lonely. David did not need her any more; neither her nor her love. Unsuspecting, feeling no nostalgic longing, he lived fully in his own heart and thoughts. She, on the other hand, lived only in memories nowadays. Her life lay almost entirely in the past, whereas David, unhampered by memories, pressed eagerly forward toward the future.

The moment she was alone with David, Michol longed to give vent to her sorrow, but she did not weep on her husband's shoulder. Instead, a dull resentment she could not explain held her back and aroused her suspicions. David might pity her and perhaps laugh at her inwardly. Going up close to him, as if she would strike him, she said in a harsh voice: "How glorious was the King of Israel today, uncovering himself before the handmaids of his servants!"

To keep back the sobs that choked her she made her voice hard. There was a sarcastic note in it that hurt David. In Michol he had always found peace and consolation. He looked at her in surprise, as if that voice and those words were a mask she had assumed. His Michol, the girl of his first love, had never before been so hostile to him.

With chin raised and eyes half-closed, she concealed her longing to weep behind a smile that offended David. He was tired and in need of a tender welcome. In times past he would have rested his head on Michol's breast and slept till daybreak. Now hurt, he, too, wanted to hurt.

"Before the Lord," he replied slowly, deliberately, "who chose me rather than thy father, and than all his house, I will both play and make myself meaner than I have done."

At mention of her father and brother Michol turned pale. Her smile was as ghastly as a wound. In spite of her hurt, she feigned scorn and indifference, and David also hardened his heart, in his stubborn determination not to let her get the better of him. Both of them weak, both weary and in need, they exaggerated their weariness, sharpening it like a weapon with which to hurt each other.

David did not realize how much sorrow lay behind his wife's gesture. She longed to fling herself at his feet weeping: "I am a poor woman. A poor woman weary and childless. My family is scattered and I am lost in loneliness. Have pity on me." But her tears, like cruel diamonds, drowned her words.

For her part, Michol no longer understood David. She had been the woman who stood by him in privation and comforted him when weary. She could not bring herself to be the woman who walked beside him in good fortune and supported him in his glory.

In youth their two souls had "clung each to the other." Now a very slender thread of jealousy divided them. David was exhausted from that festive banquet and wanted rest, but Michol herself represented the exhaustion of the banquet. She could not begin her life again at the side of a conquering and triumphant husband.

She had known the terrors of the royal palace of Gabaa, the torment of separations, the joy of reunions. She had always been torn between father and husband, between sister and brother, between husband and husband, between present and past, burning with love and frozen with terror, laughing with joy and trembling with suspicion. Now, alone and mistress of her own heart, she was lost and bewildered. She could not manage to love in good fortune as she had loved in the chaos and confusion of adversity. Even maternity, which would have upheld her in one duty and one love, had been denied her. The childless Michol would never be a mother.

The room filled with shadows, but David and Michol found no release from their exhaustion in sleep. Their faces, hardened in their determination not to yield, contrasted strangely with the intimacy of the hour.

Against the window in the reflection of the setting sun Michol's face was invisible. Neither of them spoke, but both were mentally pitying themselves.

In that sad hour of the day they grieved for their past lives and vanished youth and their disillusioned love. They pitied themselves in their hearts, but each one apart, far removed one from the other, incapable of fusing their emotions, of consoling one another.

At the first chill of night David shook off his gloomy nostalgia. He pitied Michol and her loneliness; he went close to her as if to ask forgiveness. Michol realized that his affectionate gesture meant compassion, not love. Forcing herself to one last effort, she warded him off, but in that almost saucy gesture there was a hint of tears. David smiled at her, he too, seized with sudden emotion for his unhappy wife. He brought his face close to Michol's face. And then he saw, in those staring eyes, the demented fixation of Saul and on her cheeks two traces of frozen tears.

DAVID THE SINNER

David lived in his palace in Jerusalem. Gone were the days when, in his hunger, the fugitive was glad to eat the stale, unleavened bread of sanctuary and, in his weariness and fear, to take convenient shelter in the dark caves of Judea.

In wealth and magnificence Jerusalem exceeded all the cities of Palestine. The fame of the new city and of its king had spread throughout all the East. Princes, ambassadors, and scholars came to pay their respects to David and he entertained them in his royal palace, along with musicians, singers, courtiers, and men of letters.

Life at David's court must have been unusually splendid and gay if even old Berzellai, in refusing an invitation, referred to pleasures he was no longer able to enjoy:

"I am this day fourscore years old, are my senses quick

to discern sweet and bitter? Or can meat or drink delight thy servant? Or can I hear any more the voice of singing men and singing women?"

But what had ceased to attract an old man of eighty was still pleasing to the man of fifty. David was no longer the sleepless fugitive, with clenched jaws and eyes burned by the heat of the desert. He now slept in a room lined with cedar, where the light filtered in through soft curtains and veils, where sounds were hushed by walls covered with rich tapestries, and the air was heavy with sweet perfumes.

He ate more than his once-slender body required. He drank more than his thirst demanded, but not one of those superlative wines was so delicious to him as the water that gushed at the gates of Bethlehem. He slept longer than necessary on soft furs and down pillows, and his rest was not the sound sleep of a few hours, but a prolonged and heavy torpor.

He ruled with calm severity, managing to settle ancient differences among the tribes and to overcome, appease, and exploit the patriarchal ambitions of the ancients. His knowledge of men and of how to win them with a word or a glance made it easy for him to rule his kingdom successfully.

Now that all doubts and hesitancies were allayed, everyone was convinced that the man Samuel had anointed, the conqueror of the Philistines, the man who had re-established divine service, was neither an adventurer nor a usurper. Under his rule, Israel, safe within its boundaries, united and prosperous, had become a nation.

No longer was David persecuted, harassed by enemies and slandered by malefactors. In his song to the Lord he had referred to himself many times as besieged by wild beasts and surrounded by enemies attempting to ensnare him.

"Many dogs have encompassed me," he had said in moments of great trial, or else, depicting himself as the shepherd attacked by wild beasts: "Deliver me out of the paw of the lion and the horns of the buffle."

In the dark night, particularly, sheep huddled together in a mass make a living carpet of white. Around them, restless and greedy, prowl beasts of prey. And the shepherd cannot sleep. He must stir up the fires and send out pillars of sparks that carried afar the odor of singeing. He must stand guard at the top of roads and on trails, dig ditches, and lay traps.

"He hath opened a pit," sang David, referring to his enemy, "and dug it: and he is fallen into the hole he made."

But in Jerusalem David could not say that he was surrounded "by the anguish of death." In Jerusalem he raised his voice only in songs of thanksgiving and joy. Those of prayer and anguish were forgotten.

David's citadel rested in peace. The spring gurgled merrily between the rocks, cleaving the night with a sonorous thread of silver. The king no longer watched from his palace.

The eleventh chapter of the Second Book of Kings begins with these words: "At the time when kings go forth to war . . . David sent Joab . . . "

The time when kings usually went forth to war was the spring. When for the first time thunder rolled among puffy white clouds and the first big round raindrops poured down from the heavens; when oak trees put forth new leaves and in the meadow young shoots of tender grass pushed up among drenched and twisted bushes, the kings were moved. As they looked at those heavy, silvered clouds their hearts were filled with a yearning for new pastures, and they sallied forth leading their people like sheep.

The thick fogs of winter were swept away, and in the clear, bright air new lands appeared on the horizon.

Old soldiers brought out their weapons; and as they cleaned off the ugly marks of rust the sun caught and touched off the first dazzling gleams on them. Leather shields stiffened by dampness were oiled and rubbed with mutton fat; hardened bows were made flexible, the strings renewed; the hair of their slings was stretched and made easier to handle.

To the Hebrews the time for war had come to be looked upon as the time of purification and abstinence. "If thou go out to war against thy enemies," it is written in Deuteronomy, "thou shalt abstain from all evil. If there be one among you who has become unclean during the night in sleep, let him go out from the camp and not come back until he has washed with water, in the evening. And when the sun has set, he shall return to the camp." War was not "declared" but "consecrated." Soldiers were called "the sanctified" and the unclean among them were not permitted to engage in action. The honor of being present on the day of battle had to be paid for by abstinence and purification.

God himself walked on the battlefield. The thunder was his young voice; the warm rain and the light breeze the springlike breath of his nostrils.

That spring David, in his palace, did not hear the call of war. Mist rose like clouds of smoke from the valley of Jehoshaphat, and the watercourses were clear again. But

David, shut in his chamber of cedar, enveloped in clouds of incense, did not rejoice in the burnished sky and the new-born earth.

The chatter of women and the clamor of children rose again around the bubbling fountain. War passed far away like a rain cloud watched from the citadel of Sion as one watches a storm, with fear, but also with a genuine thrill at the bottom of one's heart.

David alone remained indifferent to the din and shouting and to what was happening in the world. To him the horrors of war were ghastly crimes. He recalled with a shudder the day when he measured the Moabite prisoners, putting to death those who were too tall for the rope and keeping alive the others. Naked, stretched on the ground, the wretched creatures shrank, not in an effort to cheat, but out of sheer terror. And he had insisted on having them stretched that no man might escape his cruel fate.

He remembered the field where he had mowed and raked the Ammonites with harrows of iron. David had never violated the rules of war. Now, however, he was dismayed by it. He knew what followed the innocent laughter of spring mornings. The blood tingled at the tips of his veins, his heart beat swiftly, his whole being vibrated. One went down gaily from the high city, came to rivers, followed and crossed them; traveled through happy valleys, sighted enemy cities or the adversary's camp with a shout of keen surprise and jubilation. War seemed like one great celebration.

Then, at the first sign of resistance, his feelings of generous boldness waned. He wanted to see the enemy as pliable as rotten boughs. And with that, impulses of anger, resentment, hatred got the upper hand. The return in the summer's heat, even amid songs of victory, was not so exciting as the departure. Each man concealed a disillusionment or a remorse like a wound under his cuirass.

David did not move. In his place he sent Joab.

Joab never tired of waging war. After the battle, he held his bloodstained arms over the fire, bathed in the waters of expiation, and came back cleansed, according to the prescribed rite. He did not know what a spring without war was like. In peace his days dragged monotonously by, one like the other. For Joab night followed day and vice versa only so that fighting in the open could give place to ambushes and traps. Woods were there merely to be used for summer encampments. The valleys with twin slopes were natural arenas for battles, while the rivers followed the line of march. For him everything had some warlike significance and value.

Not even the clear, blue sky or the happy singing of birds could make him aware of the new season. His shadow told him how high the sun was; his shield warned him of the direction of the wind; but only the king informed him of the arrival ot sprıng. When the king gave Joab the sign to arm, spring burst forth in his heart. Then his face beamed with joy. His eyes shone with liquid jewels that were not tears, but fresh humors like those produced by recent pruning. Blood rushed to his cheeks, his heart swelled with kindness and generosity, and he forgot to be suspicious or jealous of his comrades at arms.

David preferred the peace of summer in Jerusalem to war.

Behold, how good and pleasant it is for brethren to dwell
together in unity:
Like the precious ointment on the head,

That ran down upon the beard, the beard of Aaron,
Which ran down to the skirt of his garment:
As the dew of Hermon,
Which descendeth upon mount Sion.

From now on he was to revel in that peace which leads to prosperity and abundance:

> Whose sons [of the just] are as new plants in their youth:
> Their daughters decked out,
> Adorned round about after the similitude of a temple:
> Their storehouses full,
> Flowing out of this into that,
> Their sheep fruitful in young,
> Abounding in their goings forth;
> Their oxen fat.
> There is no breach of wall, nor passage,
> Nor crying out in their streets.
> They have called the people happy, that hath these things:
> *But* happy is that people whose God is the Lord.

The most famous and most successful warrior of them all abhorred war and exalted peace: "Scatter thou the nations that delight in wars."

How many days he had spent in arms, how many nights in anxiety, how many years in war! But a just war signified a desire for a fruitful peace.

If you sleep among the midst of lots,
You shall be as the wings of a dove covered with silver,
And the hinder parts of her back with the paleness of gold.

However, the silver flight of peace did not spring from exhaustion, but from the slopes of Selmon whitening with bones as if from snow, while no bold flight set out from Mount Sion in the drowsiness of the morning hour to break the general atmosphere of sultriness and indifference.

A deceptive invitation of peace persuaded the king to stay at home. David's eyes were blurred by that faint glitter of gold that fills the air in summer; his ear, deafened by the persistent buzzing of eager and obstinate insects, in these days no longer clearly caught words and commands.

In those moments of false peace his will did not control his imagination or his mind his emotions. Peace was not a watchful rest in the Lord, but a weary truce between body and soul. Lured by the ease and luxury of his sumptuous palace, David the king was like those men whose

> Iniquity hath come forth, as it were from fatness;
> They have passed into the affection of the heart.

• Having eaten more than necessary and drunk more than usual, David had fallen into a deep sleep in the heat of the siesta hour on the terrace of the palace. From Jerusalem white and prostrate in that glaring sunlight no sound rose to trouble the silence of the royal citadel.

David's palace was surrounded by gardens. The tops of the trees were on a level with the palace terrace, but neither a bird nor a breath of air lighted on them. The low hum of insects lulled him to sleep and David did not awaken till late.

The sun had already touched the mountain peaks, the light wind was swaying the branches of the trees and tossing the leaves about when David awoke. Slowly, with a great effort, he roused himself from the heavy torpor that dulled his sight and hearing. To shake off that veil of sleep he began to pace up and down on the terrace.

In that grave and somnolent mood he saw, on the

terrace of a house nearby, the figure of a woman, plainly outlined against the rosy sky. At first he thought it was the light behind her revealing her figure through her filmy garments; then, from her motions and the sparkle of water, he realized that the woman, alone and seductive, was bathing herself. Leaning his elbows on the balustrade, he lingered to gaze through puffed and drowsy eyes at that figure silhouetted against the sunset.

Bethsabee belonged to the tribe of Benjamin, but she lived in Jerusalem for she was the daughter of Eliam, a courtier, and the granddaughter of Achitophel, one of the king's counsellors. Moreover, she was the wife of Urias, one of the thirty captains of the *gibborim*. She lived in the quarters reserved for officials, close to the royal palace, in David's citadel.

No doubt Eliam, her father, and Achitophel, her grandfather, had described to her the sumptuousness and delights of David's court. Those stories stirred the woman's imagination. On days of court receptions she watched the comings and goings of courtiers and, as the litters, with their attending retinues, were carried past she would run to the windows to discover the rank of the guests and the honors they would receive when they crossed the threshold of the royal palace. At night, sad and lonely on her terrace overlooking the royal gardens, she listened to the music and songs from within the palace walls.

Bethsabee pictured to herself the splendor of those receptions and the intimacy of those rooms. On the rare occasions when she was admitted with her soldier husband among the guests she was always placed in the last seats and could never get near the dignitaries and the sovereign. David had never even looked at her. And this hurt Bethsabee. She was a woman of rare beauty and unusual intelligence and she was humiliated by her position.

Urias was too much the soldier, a man trained in guerrilla warfare and hand-to-hand fighting. Like Joab he preferred war to peace. To him the bivouac was better than a dinner table, the roughness of his comrades to be preferred above the charms of women. A simple man, without culture, he neither used influence or made himself prominent at the court of the harpist-king. He, too, waited for the change of seasons to return to war. And always just before he went off to camp he would become loquacious and bold even at court. For that was the time when the king remembered his glorious veterans and honored them.

With Joab and Urias gone, the citadel became silent and tolerable again. Only Bethsabee sighed at her windows and her heart often yearned after the king when he came down to walk in his gardens. The high roof was not the best place for an evening bath, but Bethsabee chose it because of the cool breeze and in hopes that the king would notice her.

Now the Mosaic laws condemn an adultress to death by stoning. . . .

Sin is always "bitter sin." To hide his own guilt and save Bethsabee's reputation, David was obliged to stoop to a cowardly conspiracy. Well did Bethsabee know how to gain her point by improvising a scene of such despair that David, in love and deeply disturbed, would yield, unable to withstand the woman's endless sobbing. Not until Bethsabee's seductive charm and his own remorse had overcome his hesitant reluctance did the king confide in Achitophel. The latter was an astute, crafty old man, extremely intelligent and unscrupulous. His heavily lined face was like one of those hard stones covered with undecipherable hieroglyphics. Master of all tricks and a connoisseur of men, he was much sought after for advice in secret councils. He also despised Urias and felt sorry for his ambitious granddaughter.

Perhaps at the instigation of this old man, David made up his mind to have Urias killed. But to carry out his plan he had to have the help of the *sarsaba.* Urias was fighting with Joab before the walls of Rabbath.

That fact also worried David. He was loath to seek his nephew's connivance. But Bethsabee's tears and despairing sighs soon overcame his objections. Unwillingly and in disgust at himself he wrote, therefore, to Joab: "Set ye Urias in the front of the battle, where the fight is strongest; and leave ye him, that he may be wounded and die."

Then summoning Urias to the palace, he entrusted the letter to him and the faithful soldier carried his own death sentence to Joab as calmly as he would have carried an order for a reward. Not for a moment did Urias doubt the king's loyalty. Well pleased, and feeling sure that he was the bearer of important messages, the old soldier hurried from Jerusalem to Rabbath. And the nearer he came to Rabbath, the place of his doom, the more eager and pleased he was. Meanwhile, on his sullied throne, a gloomy David counted Urias' steps, and his troubled heart beat wildly.

When he read that message Joab's face lighted with joy. He, Joab, had slain Abner, an enemy; David was betraying a comrade. Joab had killed in revenge; David, out of cowardice.

Fearing lest the king repent of his order, Joab, impatient and determined not to lose this opportunity to humiliate David, quickly gathered together the army and, without provocation, led them in an assault against the walls of Rabbath. Climbing up on a height, in a firm voice he put the soldiers through the customary ritual: "What man is there that hath built a new house, and hath not dedicated it? Let him go and return to his house, lest he die in the battle, and another man dedicate it."

He looked around. No one stepped out of rank.

"What man is there that hath planted a vineyard, and hath not as yet made it to be common, whereof all men may eat? Let him go, and return to his house, lest he die in the battle and another man execute his office.

"What man is there that hath espoused a wife and not taken her? Let him go, and return to his house."

There was a long pause, then in a more resolute and ringing voice Joab added: "What man is there that is fearful and fainthearted? Let him go and return to his house, lest he make the hearts of his brethren to fear, as he himself is possessed with fear."

He looked at Urias. The captain of the *gibborim* was smiling to himself; he had not even heard the *sarsaba's* words. Joab sent him out to attack the gate of Rabbath that was most heavily defended.

The attack failed. The Israelites were thrown back and the flower of the tribe fell before the walls of the city. After the first moment of rage, Joab was afraid he had acted rashly and clumsily. To escape David's reprimand, he said, with a touch of wicked irony, to the messenger who was to bear the news of the defeat to Jerusalem: "If the king should be angry and shall say: 'Why did you go near the wall? Knew ye not that many darts are thrown from above off the wall?' Thou shalt say: 'Thy servant Urias the Hethite is also slain.' "

David as king was not subject to human laws, and no one could call him to account for Urias' life and Bethsabee's love. He had not sinned against man. He had sinned against God.

> Against thee, O Lord, I have sinned
> And have done what is evil in Thy eyes.

After Urias' death, Bethsabee left her house and lived in the palace of the king. Insolent words, ambiguous smiles, and malicious references were the comment on her presence at the king's side. Even Joab, when in David's presence, appeared unusually confident, but he would never have dared to remind him of Urias' death. No one, not even the *sarsaba,* could have reproved the king for his crime. Only one who spoke in the name of the Lord possessed that authority.

Then Nathan the prophet came to the royal palace. He was still living in a tent close to the Ark. His old age was very different from Achitophel's old age. One was the councillor of men, the other the messenger of the Lord. The one dealt in intrigues, the other destroyed them. In his human respect for rank Achitophel's words were tortuous and insinuating; confidence in his mission made Nathan bold. No touch of human jealousy could influence the conduct of the prophet who obeyed the command of a jealous God.

He spoke at first in the form of a parable:

"There were two men: the one rich, and the other poor. The rich man had exceeding many sheep and oxen. But the poor man had nothing at all but one little ewe lamb, which he had bought and nourished up. And when a certain stranger was come to the rich man, he spared to take of his own sheep and oxen, to make a feast for that stranger, but took the poor man's ewe, and dressed it for the man."

David interrupted the tale indignantly: "As the Lord liveth, the man that has done this is a child of death."

Looking hard at the king, Nathan said: "Thou art the man." Few words, quietly spoken, but incisive and revealing: "Thou art the man."

There is not a man alive who does not shudder at the injustice done by other men. There is not a man who is not quick to take revenge. And therefore all men are unjust.

Even David "rendered judgment and justice to all the people." For a slaughtered lamb he would have had the insolent thief slaughtered. He, however, had committed a greater crime.

Nathan's words opened his eyes to his sin.

Nathan did not take advantage of David's terror to overwhelm him with words. He merely added a note of bitterness softened by regret: "Why hast thou despised the word of the Lord?"

This was the word of the Lord: "Thou shalt not covet thy neighbor's wife."

And suddenly David thought with longing of his past life when he could say:

> Prove me, O Lord, and try me;
> Burn my reins and my heart.

He knew again the bitterness of sin and his disgust for it and at the same time his humiliation and his weakness. He said: "I have sinned." Those words rang with self-accusation and a confession of guilt, but mingled with a sense of such touching self-pity, humility, and submission that Nathan was moved.

When Adam's eyes were opened to his sin he was afraid. David pitied his humiliation. He was a sinner among sinners, a weak man among the weak.

For behold I was conceived in iniquity;
And in sins did my mother conceive me.

His suffering was no less keen. Casting off his royal garments, he clothed himself in sackcloth, covered his head with ashes, came down from the throne, and crouched, fasting, in a corner of the palace.

For many days and interminable nights his couch was washed with tears, tears mingled with his drink, his bread was wet with tears. His eyes were two red wounds, his hair and beard tangled in wild disorder; with livid cheeks and knees, his bones weak, his flesh emaciated, the king of Israel was unrecognizable even to his close companions. His sad song alone bore witness to the affliction of his great soul.

Have mercy on me, O God, according to thy great mercy,
And according to the multitude of thy tender mercies blot out my iniquity.

Wash me yet more from my iniquity,
And cleanse me from my sin.
For I know my iniquity,
And my sin is always before me.

Thou shalt sprinkle me with hyssop, and I shall be cleansed:
Thou shalt wash me, and I shall be made whiter than snow.
Create a clean heart in me, O God:
And renew a right spirit within my bowels.

Deliver me from blood, O God, thou God of my salvation:
And my tongue shall extol thy justice.

"First," says the Bible, "the child was struck." The fruit of the sin.

David, far from everyone, wept.

He was no longer young: moreover, the depression of age inclined him to sadness. And for that babe of a few days he felt a tenderness he could express only in tears. How much uneasiness and fear the birth of that illegitimate son had cost him! The thought of the adulteress stoned to death and of that innocent creature who would continue to live in her for a few heartbeats had perhaps driven him to write the criminal letter. That the child might live he had condemned Urias to death.

And that child of a weary father and a desperate mother had been born delicate with blue circles around his swollen eyes: a November flower. For this David had given his heart to the child, for it seemed to him that his late love and his brief passion languished in that exhausted little body.

When the signs of death marked the child's face, David had not the strength to look at him or listen to him. The child's death added pitiful torment to the sin which Nathan's words had revealed as cowardice and abomination.

David crouched in a dark corner of the palace. The sun was hateful to him, sounds frightening. He refused to touch food. The ancients came with muffled steps and urged him to get up from the ground, to take heart and to eat. David would not listen to them. The presence of men irritated him and not even the servants dared approach him.

Crouched there, shuddering with horror, he cherished in the dark the pale image of the child whom he called by name, addressing him in words more sensitive and passionate than he had ever sung to his harp or uttered on the shoulder of the beloved woman.

In the women's quarters Bethsabee, naturally domineering, became imperious. As if her son's life might be saved by her will power, she fought off sleep at night and weariness by day, her eyes wide with terror and her lips dry with anxiety. The son of the king, the son who would have raised her above all the women in Israel, must not die. She would not have it: she would not have her ambitious dreams lost with him.

Burning with fever, she ordered her handmaids about excitedly. She insisted that wise men and physicians should spend long hours watching over the little fellow's skeleton-like body. She had not even a feeling of tenderness for that son born of her flesh, and yet to instill life into him she would have gone to any lengths.

The bond with which she had tied David to her was drying out and falling like a weed burned by the sun. To Bethsabee it seemed impossible that the sickness could be stronger than her will. For seven days, hovering over the light wisp of breath which she drew almost by force from the child's breast, she refused to believe he would die. But little by little the breath grew fainter, until at last it failed to pass the transparent petal of the nostrils. The mother, seeking a sign of life, laid her head on his heart. The dull throb deceived her for a second and a chill veil passed between her cheek and the child's body.

David did not have the courage to ask about the child. He watched the servants closely, seeking in their faces a sign of improvement. He had ceased to weep. Dry-eyed, his neck stiff from watching, he tried to divine the news before it could be announced in words. He was afraid delay might distort it, and his eye, even more than his ear, was ready and alert.

He saw the servants whispering together and, jealous of

that secret which concerned him alone and which his heart already told him was true, he shouted: "Is the child dead?"

He did not wait for the vague reply. He rose, pale from fasting, filthy with ashes, staggering from lack of sleep, and demanded water to wash himself. His voice was strong, detached, inhuman.

He bathed, and put on fresh garments; calm, silent, in perfect control of himself, he gave orders and went through motions resolutely. The servants and the ancients were afraid of him. They whispered among themselves: "What thing is this that he has done? When the child was yet alive, we spoke to him, and he would not harken to our voice. Now that he is dead, he does not afflict himself nor does he weep."

And when he had washed, anointed himself, and changed his apparel, David went into the house of the Lord and fell on his knees before the Ark. And his head and his knees touched the ground at the same time.

> Thou art just, O Lord,
> And thy judgment is right.

When he stood up his face was strong and his step firm. Returned to his palace, he asked for food and he ate.

DAVID THE PROPHET

As HE grew older David began to feel that he was alone. The presence of Bethsabee in the royal palace stirred up slanders and denunciations again. David was not suspicious like Saul, but, having sinned, he was anxious and wary.

In his efforts to comfort the anguished mother, he had kept Bethsabee beside him as his favorite and she used her sorrow as a new means of dominating him. Not only that, but in her grief wily Bethsabee managed cleverly to strengthen and extend her fascination over all. Even the prophet Nathan, an enemy of Achitophel, was at first flattered then conquered by Bethsabee's feminine wiles when she entrusted him with the education of Solomon, her second and legitimate son by the king.

In that son for whom she prepared the way to the throne

by skillful intrigue, Bethsabee placed all her hopes and fears again. And David knew he could never break that silken veil of seduction the woman wove about him with her beauty and her passion.

By his sin he had brought chaos into the family and deceit into the court. The king was exhausted, bone tired. In his overpowering weariness he begged God to tell him the number of his days:

I have set a guard to my mouth,
When the sinner stood against me.
I was dumb, and was humbled, and kept silence from good
    things:
And my sorrow was renewed.
My heart grew hot within me:
And in my meditation a fire shall flame out.
O Lord, make me know my end.
And what is the number of my days:
That I may know what is wanting to me.

Behold thou hast made my days measurable:
And my substance is as nothing before thee.
And indeed all things are vanity: every man living.
Surely man passeth as an image:
Yea, and he is disquieted in vain.

He was growing old. Every night he found new lines on his face; his light blue eyes turned greenish-gray, while his thin, lifeless hair, heavy with oil, drooped on his stooping shoulders.

Before there had been any sin to burden his soul, he had thrown off every effort and every anxiety as lightly as an arrow glances off a well-oiled shield. The fierce sun that tortured the valley of the Salt Sea and carried back to the bitter lake the sweet waters which the Jordan emptied into it had neither dried nor cracked his skin. The rainstorms that dug ridges in the desert of Maon had made no impression on him and the wind from the steppes had not caused a hair of his head to fall.

In those anxious days, now long past, he had been comforted by the thought of grace.

> The law of the Lord is unspotted;
> Converting souls.

Sin, instead, had aged him. Tears of sorrow bathe but they also corrode like acid; the fire of repentance purifies, but in purifying consumes. David prayed:

> Create a clean heart in me, O God:
> And renew a right spirit within my bowels.

But the new heart and the new spirit are born of pain. God renews them not in joy but in sacrifice.

Even after David had been forgiven he lived in fear. At night the words of Nathan, the prophet, rang in his ears: "Because thou hast despised the Lord and hast taken the wife of Urias the Hethite to be thy wife the sword shall never depart from thy house."

The child had not died by the sword. His little head had drooped ever so slightly on his thin little shoulders and he had gone to rest like a withered flower. The sword was still suspended over the royal house. Where would it strike?

Amnon and Absalom, born to David of different mothers in the days when he was being persecuted and was separated from Michol, had no love for each other. Amnon had ravished Thamar, Absalom's sister by the same mother, and in addition to their rivalry for succession to the throne, which fell to Amnon as the elder, Absalom had long nourished a desire for revenge.

When the season for shearing came Absalom invited his brothers to the banquet he was giving at Baalhasor, where his sheep pastured. And he came also to David and said to him: "Behold, thy servant's sheep are shorn. Let the king, I pray, with his servants come to his servant."

But David did not accept the invitation. The memory of Nabal and the incident at Engaddi would have disturbed him and Bethsabee did not like to have memories of his past life revived to sadden the king. Abigail must be forgotten — her name wiped out forever — and her sons kept as far from their father as possible.

"If thou wilt not come," Absalom insisted, "send my brothers with me."

But even this request David refused. "It is not necessary," he said, "that Amnon should go with thee."

He knew that envy and the shame of Thamar had opened a breach of hatred between the two brothers. But Absalom was so persistent that the king finally gave his consent.

Mounted on their mules, the princes rode out of Jerusalem behind Absalom, who was mounted better than any of them. He was the life of the company.

The meadows were turning brown and the pungent scent of withered corolla was strong in the air. Herded together in the sheepfolds, the sheep stood quietly to be sheared and the strong animal odor of their wool stung the nostrils.

Absalom was gay and, to all appearances, well pleased with the shearing. He plunged his hands into the flocks of wool and tossed them lightly into the air. A few white flocks came to rest on his curly black hair — the most beautiful head of hair among the sons of David. He talked to the shepherds, laughed with them, cheered them with words and wine. Never had he been so merry and loquacious.

At the banquet he mixed drinks recklessly. His brothers laughed with him and drank with no thought of the death which, in Absalom's mind, weighed as heavy as dregs of wine.

To his servants he said: "Take notice and when you see Amnon drunk, strike him and kill him."

The servants did as he commanded. At the end of the banquet when Amnon, much the worse for wine, tried in vain to rise, they closed in around him and killed him. The other brothers, whose heads were also fuddled and their legs and arms heavy, did not even go to his defense. Mad with terror, they ran for their mules, flung themselves on their backs, and dashed helter-skelter for the open country.

The news reached David much exaggerated. Word of the fratricide was known in Jerusalem before the brothers arrived: "Absalom has slain all the king's sons and there is not one of them left." The sword David had seen suspended over the family had fallen!

David rose from his throne and, without a cry, as if a hand grasped him by the throat, he fell face downward on the stairs, while his servants rent their garments and raised a fearful wailing that re-echoed mournfully in the women's quarters. Only Bethsabee, pale with emotion, clutching little Solomon to her breast, did not weep, but she trembled at the tragic fulfillment of her plans.

Later, covered with dust, stunned and frightened, the surviving brothers arrived. David embraced them, calling each one of them by the name of Amnon and weeping.

After killing his brother, Absalom fled to the King of Gessur and David lost two sons at the same time: Amnon dead, Absalom banished.

Three years the court mourned, after which, through Joab's intercession, Absalom was recalled from exile. But for two more years the fratricide was forbidden "to see the face of David," and he fretted and fumed because he was not allowed to frequent the palace.

Absalom was exceedingly beautiful. In all Israel there was not a man so comely. From the soles of his feet to the crown of his head there was no blemish on him. When his long, curly hair was cut (once a year, the Bible says, because it was burdensome to him) the hair fell in thick, lustrous curls, leaving a mountain of perfumed ebony on the ground.

Charming and expansive in manner, his elegance and vanity won him the sympathy and affection of everyone with whom he came in contact. Without him, after the death of Amnon, the king's palace seemed dismal and grim.

Absalom felt humiliated at being forced to lead the life of a private citizen in Jerusalem and he tried to persuade the *sarsaba* to intercede again for him with the king. Joab was not in favor with Bethsabee. To David and to Solomon's mother he was a constant reminder of those days of sin and terror when Urias fought before the walls of Rabbath. He knew the secret surrounding Urias' heroic death, and he could have repeated word for word the contents of that letter David had written and Bethsabee had perhaps dictated in terror of being stoned.

All of Bethsabee's efforts to win over the fierce old soldier to her side and to Solomon's party failed when confronted with Joab's firm character. He did not covet any of the palace honors Bethsabee dispensed. He despised that atmosphere of heavy devotion that surrounded the young prince, raised by a woman and by a priest. Joab was growing old: he preferred Saul's method to the way David behaved. The king's anxious, pensive face disappointed and irritated him.

Absalom took advantage of Joab's intolerance to win him to his side, though the *sarsaba* had no love either for the secret maneuvers of that ambitious young prince. When Absalom sent for Joab to ask him to intercede with the king, the old *sarsaba* refused to come. Absalom then ordered his servants to set fire to Joab's ripe fields, thus repeating in miniature and at an inopportune moment Samson's gesture. At that, Joab hurried to the prince to demand reprisal, but Absalom, smiling condescendingly, pointed out that the fire had been the one certain means of making Joab accept his invitation.

With difficulty Joab refrained from one of his fierce outbursts. He fixed his eagle eye on Absalom's rosy countenance. If that flourishing young man were to die Bethsabee would be pleased, but David would be deeply grieved. For that reason he controlled his impulse. But from that moment perhaps there grew in him a feeling of resentment against the arrogant young prince.

Recalled to the palace again, Absalom was grateful neither to Joab nor to David. He sought popular favor and found no better way to win fame and a following than to criticize his father's government.

Every morning he went to the city gates. In the early morning light the walls looked white; the high palaces and the royal castle glistened in the sun. To the west, the deep, narrow valley of Jehoshaphat still lay hidden in the shadows of night. And out of that cool shade figures emerged into the bright sunlight the moment they crossed the ditch: men headed for the capital, mounted on mules or asses; or coming down from the tribes to the north to protest against too heavy a tax or complain of an abuse.

In reorganizing the government, David had left the tribes autonomous, but had tampered with a number of private interests; and this gave rise to much dissatisfaction and quarreling, particularly among the northern tribes to whom David was only a "Jew." From the south, however, men of Juda and of Benjamin arrived at the gates of the city. The former complained that David did not show enough favor to his native tribe. The latter regretted Saul's military rule and refused to pay tributes for worship and for the temple.

So now Absalom betook himself to the city gates because that was where justice was administered. There the ancients still sat beside the gates to hear private quarrels; and as someone was always the loser, the gates were crowded with malcontents. Like all people who feel they are misunderstood and abused, the malcontents were eager to talk and the more they talked the more they were convinced they were right.

Absalom encouraged their complaints by listening to them interestedly and, as it were, in silent agreement. When they had finished, he would say: "Thy words seem to me good and just. But there is no man appointed by the king to hear thee." Then, after a silence, he would sigh and add: "Oh, that they would make me judge over the land!"

When the Israelites returned to their tribes and villages at night, almost all of them disillusioned or discouraged, they would repeat with conviction: "Oh, if Absalom were made judge over all Israel!"

By his conduct Absalom showed his eagerness to make a good reputation throughout all the land. "When any man came to salute him," says the Bible, "he put forth his hand, and took him, and kissed him."

David had also been young, handsome, and charming, but the beauty and charm of Absalom were not like his father's. Absalom was a great talker and abhorred solitude and he enjoyed his own wit and eloquence. His features were regular, carved like a statue, and when he spoke only the curve of his lips would move sinuously. His impassive eyes and fleshy nose gave his whole face an outward beauty but one without depth.

Even as an old man David had not lost his charm, which was if anything intensified by the sadness that comes from consciousness of sin. He suffered for that son whom he loved above all the others, because of his beauty and also because of his ingratitude. His son's speeches with all their boasts, criticisms, and promises were duly reported to him. David was grieved, but not offended. Because he was afraid the scenes of jealousy in the royal palace of Gabaa might be repeated in his palace at Jerusalem he was inclined to be overly indulgent to his son. In his effort not to be unjust he laid himself open to slander. Only in song did he complain to God:

> They that sat at the gate spoke against me:
> And they that drank wine made me their song.

He vented his bitterness in song, and as he sang he was comforted, for suddenly his songs were transformed from laments into songs of prophecy.

More and more David lost the earthly appearance of a king and assumed the tone and the importance of a prophet. It was as if his eyes had ceased to see the things around him, but read in the centuries the glory of a reign compared to which his throne was covered with mire.

At night, when the citadel slept and Absalom's noisy boasting had ceased to echo in the royal palace, David rose up to sing of his own sorrows and to confess his own emotions. But as if his hand had lost the power to pluck the chords and his mind was no longer filled with bold imaginings, his song took off on metaphoric flights, exaggerating incidents at court and in the city, not from overemphasis, but through his power of prophecy.

David no longer lived the life of a man, but of "a royal prophecy"; no longer the life of a king, but of an inspired prophet. His poetic expressions transcended present reality and announced the advent of a future reality:

Why did the Gentiles rage,
And the people meditate vain things?
The kings of the earth stood up,
And the princes assembled together
Against the Lord, and his Christ.

Let us break their bonds asunder:
And let us cast away their yoke from us.
He that dwelleth in heaven shall laugh at them:
And the Lord shall deride them.
Then shall he speak to them in his anger,
And trouble them in his rage.
"But I am appointed king by him
Over Sion his holy mountain,
Preaching his commandment."
The Lord hath said to me: Thou art my son,
This day have I begotten thee.

Ask of me, and I will give thee the Gentiles
for thy inheritance,
And the utmost parts of the earth for thy possession,
Thou shalt rule them with a rod of iron,
And shalt break them in pieces like a potter's
vessel.

David paid no heed to pomp and ceremony or to guests. Absalom, instead, splendidly dressed, held a court of his own. He gave magnificent banquets; made a great show of fine chariots and horses. Horses, in particular, were his major luxury.

The Hebrews had never owned horses. They had camels, asses, beasts of burden and work animals. To them the horse represented the luxury animal, while the work animal was the ass, whose hard, straight rump made one stiff, solid line from tail to head.

The horse's strength and beauty had to be maintained by good food and assiduous care. With his legs as frail as glass, his back as supple as a willow, his mane as delicate as a woman's head of hair, the flashing, quivering horse neighed and reared at the rattle of arms and the blare of trumpets. He pawed the ground impatiently and foamed at the mouth. As generous as the ass was calculating, as impetuous as the ass was reluctant, he was as much a delight as the ass was sulky and headstrong. The Hebrews admired the horse, but they harnessed their ass and loaded him fondly with packsaddles. They, too, were gloomy and headstrong.

To the prophets, guardians of tradition, the horse was an animal ever alien to the temperament of the Hebrew people. "And it shall come to pass in that day," says Micheas, "that [the Lord] will take away thy horses out of the midst of [Israel], and will destroy thy chariots." And Isaias bewailing the vices of vanity: "And their land is filled with horses and their chariots are innumerable.... Woe to them that go down to Egypt for help, trusting in horses!"

Absalom, on the other hand, loved horses. He liked to press his cheek against their glossy necks and, running his hand over their high withers, enjoy the play of their sensitive ears. The crunch of the bit in the horse's mouth made a hollow and rather pleasant sound.

He himself led his horses to the fountain. Plunging his bared arm into the still water, he stirred it and guided the horse's dark underjaw down to skim the chill surface. Then, still holding the reins, he walked back beside his horse to David's citadel. The clatter of iron hoofs on the pavement was sweet music to which Absalom kept step with the swiftness of a horseman afoot.

The greatest number of malconents were to be found in Hebron because David had deserted the city to build his new city on the Jebusites' rocks. In Hebron his first sons had been born: Amnon, Cheleab, Absalom, Adonis, Safatia, Jetraan. To Hebron came the tribes farthest from Juda to pay their respects. Enlarged and beautified in the seven years and a half of his reign, Hebron had been on the way to becoming the most important city in Palestine when David abandoned it.

After that it declined sadly and exhausted its newfound wealth. On his departure David left behind him in Hebron disappointed ambitions, ruined fortunes, regrets.

The Hebronites could not appreciate David's reasons for laying the foundations of his capital on the Mount of Sion. They considered him ungrateful, and Absalom kindled their wrath by showing his own attachment to the city of his birth and his regret at leaving it. If the young prince had led a life of pomp and splendor in Jerusalem, in Hebron he lived quietly and nostalgically. He would stroll along the old walls, recalling the past glories of the city as well as memories of his childhood. The sight of the places where his family had stayed and to which David had never returned after his entrance into Jerusalem, moved him deeply.

How many memories that city held! There David had been crowned; there he had received the submission of the tribes; there Abner had brought Michol back to him; and there Abner had been slain by Joab.

"If I am king," Absalom promised, "I shall come to Hebron to be crowned where my father was crowned." And the Hebronites would have rejoiced to hasten that day. For that reason, when the moment to revolt against his father came, Absalom chose Hebron as the center of the uprising.

To David he said: "Let me go and pay my vows which I have vowed to the Lord in Hebron." To others he said instead: "As soon as you shall hear the sound of the trumpet, say ye: Absalom reigneth in Hebron."

The trumpets blared, horses neighed, and the people of Hebron rallied round the son of David who had turned against his father. The sunset of Goliath's slayer began more miserably than Saul's. That gloomy royal palace, saddened by psalms, would miss Absalom's youthful gaiety!

A messenger hastened to Jerusalem to take the news to David. "All Israel with their whole heart followeth Absalom."

That was not true: the heart of Israel still beat for the old king. Nevertheless David reeled under that blow. He did not curse Absalom, and at the thought that now the rebel would never reign he was filled with pity for his son.

Vain is the horse for safety
Neither shall he [the horseman] be saved by the abundance
of his strength.

He knew that the victory would be his, but he could neither rejoice nor threaten. Once again he was confronted with the painful alternative of those days when he had been pursued by Saul. He could not hate his enemy, and in his hope, even more his certainty, of victory, there was an element of pity.

The son conceived in sin, the most beautiful young man in the family, the favorite prince of all the court, had rebelled against his father the king. David loved Absalom more than any of his sons. When he ran his hand lightly over Absalom's hair, when he looked into his shining eyes, when he followed the curve of those sinuous lips, he forgot his son's cruelty and ingratitude. Absalom submitted to his father's caresses, but his eyes hardened and his lips narrowed in irritation. He was afraid of Bethsabee's tricks and in his heart he blamed his father for allowing himself to be swayed by that intriguing woman.

That suspicion lay at the root of Absalom's rebellion. David knew this, but he could not dissuade his son from that plan which, instead of thwarting Bethsabee, facilitated her success.

Against an Absalom in revolt, David was forced to mete out harsh punishment. Pity for his son, compassion for his youth, his own anguish for his flesh and blood, made that punishment doubly painful but no less necessary.

David stood up and with a gesture of despair said: "Arise and let us flee." Then, baring his feet, he covered his head in sign of mourning, girded a rope of hemp around his loins, and went forth from the palace. The citadel swarmed with soldiers; they drew apart to let the king pass. David scarcely raised his eyes to the towers. It seemed that the birds screaming in swift flight could not bear the rawness of that glassy air.

David passed through the streets of Jerusalem, between high palaces only partially awake but already stunned by the news of the day. Word of Absalom's revolt and of David's departure spread through all the highways and byways of the city. This was the second time David's son had caused Jerusalem anguish. The report that the king's sons had been murdered had spread like wildfire, licking and roaring as it went. The announcement of the revolt, on the other hand, was received in stunned silence. The people stood along the streets as the king passed by, knelt in silence, and wept.

With bowed head, as if his son's guilt were his own, David fled from his royal palace and from the city. He had only one desire — to be alone in his sorrow. The sons of Sarvia still followed him. They were old, too, but when they heard that the king was leaving, they buckled on their armor and hurried to the palace, with the same devotion as on the day their mother led them to the cave of Odollam.

At the gates David noticed that Etai, head of his guards, a regiment of Philistine mercenaries, also followed behind him. David stopped him: "Why comest thou with us? Thou art a stranger. I shall go whither I am going, but return thou and the Lord shew thee mercy and justice as thou hast shewn grace and fidelity with me."

But Etai replied: "In what place soever thou shalt be, either in death or in life, there will thy servant be."

David looked at him. The Philistine's clear, innocent eyes shone with a calm and peaceful light. He looked like a giant baby, with his long blond hair hanging on his shoulders as was the custom among his people. As David looked at him, the light in Etai's eyes trembled and two big tears rolled down on the soldier's beard.

"Come, and pass over," David said to him, and with him he went out through the gates of Jerusalem.

At that moment the Levites, wearing their short tunics and carrying the Ark of the Covenant on flexible shafts, came up. David stopped them: "If I shall find grace in the sight of the Lord," he said to them, "and if He shall deign to call me back to Jerusalem, I shall return. If not, let Him do that which is good before Him."

The messenger had arrived at the city just as the gates were opened. David had made his decision without asking anyone's advice or opinion. The sun was therefore not yet high in the sky when he went out from Jerusalem while his people stood on the walls and wept.

As David, still barefooted and with his head covered, climbed the Hill of Olives, near Gethsemane, he learned that Achitophel, Bethsabee's grandfather, had deserted him and gone over to Absalom. David knew how keenly intelligent that clever, unscrupulous old man was. But he did not even curse him. He merely said: "Foil, O Lord, I beseech thee, the counsel of Achitophel."

At the top of the hill an old man by the name of Chusai, whom the Bible calls "the friend of David," came toward him. With Nathan, Chusai headed the party opposing

Achitophel; now he came to offer his services to David. But the king urged him to return to Jerusalem, and without counsellors, accompanied by his nephews and followed by a vast army of soldiers, David went on his way, walking in the direction of the desert.

The sun was hot, David's throat was parched with thirst, but he did not ask for drink. Abstracted, his thoughts far away, he plodded along. Toward evening, afar off and silhouetted against the setting sun, they saw a man coming toward them. He was of the kindred of the house of Saul and his name was Semei. When he heard that David had abandoned the capital and fled in the garb of a penitent, he came out to insult him.

> My strength is dried up like a potsherd,
> And my tongue hath cleaved to my jaws:
> And thou hast brought me down
> Into the dust of death.

On that long walk, weeping and thirst had parched the king's throat. Drops of saliva ran out of the corners of his mouth, mingling with the dust upon his face. Semei was pleased to see David reduced to such a miserable state, with his head covered and his feet dusty, and while still some distance off he began to throw stones at him. "The Lord hath repaid thee for what thou hast done to Saul."

Though David could not recognize the man, he made no effort to hide either his dejection or his weariness.

> They have numbered all my bones
> And they have looked and stared upon me.

Semei approached and said with a sneer: "The Lord hath repaid thee for all the blood of the house of Saul and behold thy evils press upon thee."

David raised his sorrowful eyes to his persecutor. He recognized him for one of those cowards who dare to be bold only when others are in trouble. He paid no attention to him and did not reply.

All they that saw me have laughed me to scorn:
They have spoken with the lips, and wagged the head.
"He hoped in the Lord, let him deliver him:
Let him save him, seeing he delighteth in him."

In a voice hoarse from his violent outburst, Semei cried almost in the king's ear: "Why dost thou not call on thy salvation now? Why hast thou ceased to be the favorite?"

The sons of Sarvia waited with their hands on the hilts of their swords for David to turn toward them. One sign from him and Semei would have had his head severed from his body as quickly as if he were a mad dog. But David did not raise his head, neither did he turn around. On the contrary, he seemed to be listening even more intently to that insulting voice.

Furious at Semei and even angrier at the king's attitude, Abisai intervened with his usual violence: "Why should this dog dare to curse the lord, my king? I will go and cut off his head."

He started forward, his sword bared, but David stopped him. Proudly, his head held high, his face strong and energetic, eyes cold as in moments of command, eyebrows contracted and forehead stormy, David nailed him before he had gone two steps. "What have I to do with you, ye sons of Sarvia?" he said resolutely. "Let him curse, for the Lord hath bid him curse David."

The way led uphill again, the sun had set, and the crest of the mountain stood out against a line of fire. David continued on up the hill. Semei went ahead of him, and walking backward, he threw stones at the king's bare feet. The blood streamed from David's ankles and feet as he repeated in a low tone the verses of the passion:

> The council of the malignant hath besieged me,
> They have dug my hands and feet.

Semei also threw clumps of earth and dust in his face and on his head. David, who was already suffering from thirst, complained in strange words that do not sound like him:

> And they gave me gall for my food,
> And in my thirst they gave me vinegar to drink.

In places where the going was hard, on the steepest cliffs, Semei tugged at his garments, scoffed at him and shoved him off the road. And David said:

> They parted my garments amongst them,
> And upon my vesture they cast lots.

Sweating and bleeding, drenched with perspiration and covered with dust, with his garments torn, humiliated, almost dead from exhaustion, David finally reached the mountain top just as night settled down over all the land. The sky hung lowering over the wan and hidden countryside. The few torches behind the king made the night even darker. David fell on his knees and, uncovering his head, lifted his face to something the night hid from him:

> My God, my God, why hast thou forsaken me?
> Far from my salvation are the words of my sin.

By abandoning Jerusalem David proved that he was still a good strategist. In his youthful impatience, Absalom would have seized the capital and captured David among the enemies both inside the city and without. On the other hand, in withdrawing toward the desert David repeated the maneuver by which he had conquered the Philistine army. He had left the Ark of the Covenant in Jerusalem in the hope of maintaining at least a semblance of order and discipline in the city. Finally old Chusai, whom he had refused to allow to follow him, would be, he thought, a foil for Achitophel's insidious council.

When the revolt broke out, David had been neither strong nor confident: he had been prostrated with grief; his followers dismayed; while those who were lukewarm had waited to see which way the victory would go.

Spurred on by ambition, Absalom entered Jerusalem at once. He rode up through the streets of the new city, took the citadel easily by storm, and presented himself at the royal palace as the ruler. That palace his father had closed to him for years on end after Amnon's assassination now became his dominion. Achitophel, his wrinkled old face bent on evil, followed Absalom as more than once the young prince hesitated before a door or in front of David's harp or his spear, but Achitophel urged him to be bold. The old man abetted this youth who was so eager to play the master, but always a little timorous — even in the women's quarter.

Along with the vicious advice to dishonor the women of his father's household, old Achitophel gave Absalom one wise piece of advice: to attack David immediately in the desert before he could recover from his surprise and prostration. He knew the king's temperament. In David grief was stronger than anger, and counsel ruled his passions.

Absalom did not heed Achitophel's advice. Instead, he listened to Chusai who, as David's friend, offered the opposite opinion: "Thou knowest thy father, and the men that are with him, that they are very valiant, and bitter in their mind, as a bear raging in the wood when her whelps are taken away. Let all Israel be gathered to thee, as the sand of the sea which cannot be numbered: and thou shalt be in the midst of them. And we shall come upon him in what place soever he shall be found: and we shall cover him, as the dew falleth upon the ground, and we shall not leave of the men that are with him not so much as one."

"The counsel of Chusai," said Absalom, who liked flowery speech, "is better than the counsel of Achitophel."

He was mistaken. The portrait Chusai had treacherously drawn of David could not have been more deceptive. David had never behaved like "a bear raging in the wood." But Absalom was not a soldier. He preferred ringing words to wise counsel. He accepted Chusai's plan and turned down Achitophel's.

The old councillor realized that the son was not the equal of the father he had betrayed. At first he was seized with raging scorn, then with mute despair. From that moment Absalom's cause, for which Achitophel had deserted David, declined. Achitophel had returned "evil for good" to David by turning his son against him, by helping the rebel, and giving him evil advice. He had been a traitor in his old age, with no hope of rehabilitation and no possibility of victory. He believed that David would never forgive him.

All night long he stayed awake, a prey to despair and anger. In the morning, while the palace was still asleep, he went out into the ash-colored air. With his eyes dark under heavy gray eyebrows, his deep wrinkles and stooping shoulders, he saddled his ass, mounted, and rode furtively out of Jerusalem.

He rode toward his native city of Gilo, and when he came to his house he refused to see anyone. Coldly he set about disposing of his possessions, and when evening came, he locked himself in his bedroom and hanged himself.

David waited for Absalom to cross the Jordan and be the first to attack. He did not want to take part in the battle; so he placed Joab and Abisai in the front of his army, and begged them to be merciful. He talked anxiously with each of his captains, one by one, and placed his hand on their shoulders: "Spare my son Absalom."

The battle was fought in the forest of Ephraim and the rebels were defeated. Absalom was mounted on a mule, not a horse. Perhaps he feared the horse might carry him too far forward in battle. Prudence had probably advised the safer and more circumspect mule.

In the retreat, however, the mule's prudence turned into wild, headlong flight. Indifferent to the wrench of the twitch and the torment of the bit, with neck straining forward and tail rigid, the frightened animal plunged through the woods heedless of ground and obstacles. In that mad race Absalom's heavy head of hair flew out behind. As they passed under the low bows of an oak his hair caught in between two branches. Absalom screamed. The mule dashed on ahead and the king's ambitious son was left hanging between the treetops and the ground.

A soldier caught sight of him, but he did not dare to kill him. He told Joab, and the latter, disregarding David's fervent injunctions, chose three sharp javelins and plunged them into Absalom's heart. Then he ordered the dead body cut down from the branches. Flinging it into a grave in the woods he covered it over with stones.

David had stayed behind in the city. Since dawn he had been sitting between the two gates of Ephraim. His face maintained its usual composure; only his hands moving restlessly on his knees, the scarred and supple hands of the harpist, betrayed his suffering. Leaning against the wall, he looked out over the land, which was coming slowly into view in the dull and misty morning. The woods, where the battle was being waged, was barely visible in the midst of all the other green. It seemed to be a low stand of tamarisks and junipers.

David peered anxiously at that motionless green that neither wind nor the onrush of battle stirred. Impenetrable and indifferent, the woods showed no sign of the struggle.

In the distance shepherds could be seen driving their sheep, scattered by the fighting, on to fallow lands, and from their movements David could judge the direction of the battle. Fear gripped him at the thought of Joab's face as he gave furious chase in the depths of the woods, and he groaned and wondered where Absalom was. He hoped the low-hanging oaks had hidden him from the eyes of Sarvia's sons or that he had found safety near the top of the mountain, among the shepherds.

Scanning the edge of the woods again, he saw a few stragglers come out of the thick of the fight and venture into the fields. From their gestures and the direction they took David tried in vain to guess the outcome of the battle. His eyes ached from straining; his jaws, clenched in a nervous spasm, pained; his face turned yellow. Just then the sentry in the gate tower saw a man emerge from the woods and run toward the city. He called David's attention to him. The man was running through the open fields, therefore he could not be carrying arms. "He is a messenger," said David, "and if he is alone, he brings good news."

The runner had not yet reached the gate when the sentry reported that another man, alone and unarmed, was running after the first man. "He also has good news," said the king.

When the first messenger came within hearing distance he shouted: "God save thee, O King." It was the announcement of victory.

With his tongue cleaving to his palate, his throat dry, and his voice hoarse, David went to meet him and asked: "Is my son Absalom safe?" It was then he learned that his son was dead.

Pale as death, he stood. His eyes were sunken alarmingly in his head. His lips stuck to his dry teeth, and his hands hung limp at his sides. With difficulty he reached the guardroom near the city gate and shut himself in. Those outside heard him groan: "My son, Absalom, Absalom my son: would to God that I might die for thee, Absalom my son, my son Absalom."

The sentinels on the walls were suddenly overcome by the enervating heat of that foggy day. They gave up their watch and sat with their aching heads clasped in their hands. Then they heard that lament coming from below through the wall: "My son, Absalom, Absalom my son," and they found that their hands were wet with tears.

The soldiers who came back from the battle leaned against the walls like beggars at sunset. They did not have the heart to pass through the gate. They did not have the courage to face that grief. All day long they had fought, wounded, killed, lost comrades and relatives. Their bodies ached from the weight of their armor; they were covered with bruises, with wounds, but the grief of that heart-broken father was greater than any pain: "My son, Absalom, Absalom, my son!"

It seemed as if the weeping would never end. For Saul and for Jonathan, David had rent his garments, had taken up his harp and intoned the *quinah*. On the death of Abner he had cursed furiously. For the death of his son he had not even the strength to tear the ephod of flax into pieces; he had not even the energy to lift the harp. With his forehead pressed against the wall, he wept. His tears flowed as if from the wall of an old cistern. And in the midst of the tears only one lament, monotonous, childish, insistent: "Absalom, my son, my son Absalom!"

Victory was transformed into mourning. The misty day became the thick fog of evening and the people said: "The king grieveth for his son who is dead." Even victories hurt.

To crush the rebellion David had murdered his son. Now he wept. The harshness of justice was dissolved in tears.

Joab, the sword of Israel, came to the gates of Ephraim. He, too, was told: "The king mourns." He, too, heard that pitiful lament, imprisoned in the wall, but he was not moved by it. On the contrary, that mourning and the melancholy it aroused surprised him. Looking about, he saw the soldiers disheartened, the people grief-stricken, and he was indignant.

Joab and his sword were inseparable; not a spot of blood ever remained on the blade. It flashed at the end of the battle as it had flashed in the beginning. In hand-to-hand fighting the gleam of the sword was lightly reddened by a veil of blood, constantly renewed.

When he learned that the king, on hearing of the victory, had shut himself in the guardroom, Joab could not control his uneasiness. He went straight to the door. "The king mourns," the sentinels told him. Joab did not stop. He had no hesitation. He knocked at the door and so loudly that the noise covered the sound of David's weeping.

For the first time he was bold enough to come before the king with words of reproach. "Thou hast shamed this day," he said; "the faces of all thy servants. Thou lovest them that hate thee, and thou hatest them that love thee. If Absalom had lived, and we had all been slain, would it have pleased thee?"

Surprised at his nephew's arrogance, David raised his head. He took his forehead from the wall; he ceased his lament. His aversion for his nephew increased a hundredfold, but this time there was more than ruthlessness in Joab's words.

He, David, was the king. Joab's voice reminded him of his neglected duty. David did not belong to David, nor to his grief as a father.

"Now therefore arise," Joab commanded, "arise and go out and speak to the satisfaction of thy servants."

David arose. His limbs were stiff and sore; body and soul ached. He followed Joab outside the walls. Dark night had blotted out the land and the woods were not visible.

In the mystery of night, sorrow alone seemed to reign over the world. And that sorrow was filled with the might of another Kingdom established forever on sacrifice.

Joab ordered a throne, fashioned together by pikes and secured with shields, to be set up against the walls of the city. And on that throne David sat while, in the night, by hundreds and by thousands, faceless soldiers, an endless army, passed before him shouting: "Long live the King of Israel."

BIBLIOGRAPHICAL NOTE

THE author of this book lays no claim either to knowledge of Hebrew, training in Sacred Scripture, or competence in Biblical exegesis.

In compiling this bibliographical note he wishes, first of all, to thank Father Giuseppe Messina, professor at the Istituto Biblico and that superb translator, Father Alberto Vaccari, for the invaluable aid they have so kindly given him.

For the Bible story the author consulted the following works: Martini's now classic translation, and the more modern translations of various scholars (Bonaccorsi, Castoldi, Giovanozzi, Mezzacasa, Ramorino, Ricciotti, Zampini) published by the Libreria Editrice Fiorentina, also Father Paul Dhorme, *Les livres de Samuel:* Lecoffre, Paris, 1910.

For the poetical books: Father Alberto Vaccari's translation, *I libri poetici della Bibbia,* Pontificio Istituto Biblico, Rome, 1925, and Father Giuseppe Ricciotti's excellent anthology, *Dalla Bibbia,* Zanichelli, Bologna, 1921.

For the history of the people of Israel, Father Giuseppe Ricciotti's *Storia d'Israele,* Vol. II, Società Editrice Internazionale, Turin, 1932; Adolphe Lods' *Israël, dès origines au milieu du VIII siècle,* La Renaissance du Livre, Paris, 1932, and L. Desnoyers' *Histoire du peuple hébreu,* Picard, Paris, 1930.

Other sources consulted were: Frazer, *Le Folklore dans l'Ancien Testament* (translation by Audra), Genther, Paris,

1924. For descriptions of the country and the life of that day: Roberto Almagia, *Palestina,* Rome, 1930; G. A. Smith, *The Historical Geography of the Holy Land,* Hodder, London, 1931; S. Neil, *Everyday Life in the Holy Land,* Cassell, London, 1931; C. T. Wilson, *Peasant Life in the Holy Land,* Murray, London, 1906; R. Lees, *Village Life in Palestine,* Longmans Green, London, 1907.

This present volume was already in proof when Israele Zolli's book: *Israele, studi storici-religiosi,* Istituto delle Edizione academiche, was published in Udine.

Is there a literature on David? The author has found nothing in the Italian language, if one excepts the fine article on "David" by Father Giuseppe Ricciotti in the *Enciclopedia Italiana;* only two books in French and one in German.

The first French book is by Cardinal Meignau — *David roi, psalmiste, prophète,* Lecoffre, Paris, 1893. It is a polemic against Renan *(Histoire du peuple d'Israël,* Calmann-Levy, Paris, 1887), who depicted Jesus' ancestor as a lucky impostor. The second is by Marcel Dieulafoy — *Le Roi David,* Hachette, Paris, 1897. This is a careful study of the institutions of the Kingdom of Israel and of its military organizations in particular.

The German book, translated recently into French and published by Payot, is the posthumous work of Professor B. Baentsch of the University of Jena. It follows, paragraph for paragraph, the Books of Kings, and is carefully documented.

The author did not wish to burden his book with notes, almost all of which would have referred to the Book of Ruth and the first two Books of Kings, with occasional reference to the two books of the Paralipomenon and more rarely to Genesis, Exodus, Leviticus, Deuteronomy, Joshua and Judges.

For David the sinner, the author consulted St. Ambrose's beautiful *Apologia* (Migne, *Patrologia Latina,* Vol. XIV, page 890).

NIHIL OBSTAT: JOHN M. A. FEARNS, S.T.D., *Censor Librorum*

IMPRIMATUR: ✠ FRANCIS CARDINAL SPELLMAN, *Archbishop of New York*

New York
February 15, 1954